# Gentleman Traitor

# Gentleman Traitor

HARCOURT
BRACE
JOVANOVICH

ALAN WILLIAMS

NEW YORK AND LONDON

# Gentleman Traitor

HARCOURT
BRACE
JOVANOVICH

ALAN WILLIAMS

NEW YORK AND LONDON

Printed in the United States of America


Library of Congress Cataloging in Publication Data

Williams, Alan, 1935—
    Gentleman traitor.

    I. Title.
PZ4.W714Ge3  [PR6073.I4258]    823'.9'14    75–15791
ISBN 0–15–135015–9

First American edition 1975
B C D E

*For Audrey, with love*

# Gentleman Traitor

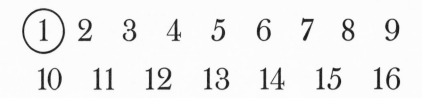

*It was a quiet evening at Hillcrest.* Mrs. Ross-Needham finished spraying the roses and walked up the gravel path through the African dusk, past two boys who were folding up deck chairs on the front lawn. Ground mist was rising from the valley, curling like smoke round the stout tree trunks. In a few minutes it would be dark. On the edge of the swimming pool a third boy sat on his heels and skimmed insects off the surface of the water with a net.

Mrs. Ross-Needham stepped through the porch into the hotel and smiled at one of the guests, a bald chubby man who was starting up the stairs to change for dinner. "Good evening, Mr. Prentice. It has been a lovely day, hasn't it?"

"It certainly has, Mrs. Ross-Needham."

In the lounge half a dozen men sat reading back numbers of the *Illustrated London News* or fidgeting with crosswords. They raised their heads to acknowledge Mrs. Ross-Needham's smile, as she passed through to the bar where her husband was unlocking the till and arranging the tape recorder—forty minutes of unbroken melodies from popular postwar musicals.

"Everything all right, Jack?"

He nodded. "Campbell hooked a real whopper up at Leopard Ridge this afternoon. Wouldn't mind betting it's a four-pounder. I've given it to the cook, and we're promised some for lunch tomorrow."

"That's nice of him. Seen anything of Mr. Fielding?"

"Not a thing since lunch. Three double gins and a bottle of Mateus. Probably sleeping it off. Trouble with a chap like that, doesn't take any exercise. Like a drink, dear?"

"I think I'll wait." She sat on a stool across the bar from him and watched while he poured himself a gin-and-tonic. "I feel rather sorry for him," she said. "He told Mr. Prentice that he's recently a widower. Though I notice he doesn't wear a ring."

"All I can say," replied her husband, "is that for a drinking man he's damned unsociable. Don't think I've had more than a dozen words with him since he got here. Must be over a week now."

"Six days." She smiled. "He arrived on Tuesday the tenth and took the Hamiltons' old room, remember?"

"How long's he plan staying?"

"He wasn't sure. He said it might be three weeks to a month." Mrs. Ross-Needham gave a small frown. "You've nothing against him, have you, Jack?"

"Only that I like to see people enjoying themselves. In Fielding's case I wouldn't be surprised if the chap was an alcoholic—and we've both seen a few of them around, haven't we? His bar bill would do justice to old Nick Robson! Still, mustn't complain—all in a day's work." He grinned over his glass. "Sure you wouldn't like that drink, dear?"

"I think I'll get changed," she said, slipping off the stool and smoothing her dress. "Dinner in half an hour. And I must have a word with cook about that dessert—last night's was quite awful!"

As she turned, two men in crested blazers came in talking loudly. They paused to greet her, then called to her husband: "The usual, Jack. And don't be too generous with the lime!"

"You know me, Tommy," Ross-Needham growled, and they all laughed.

Jack and Ingrid Ross-Needham were a popular couple. They had married at the end of the war in Copenhagen—she was a local girl of nineteen, he a young subaltern with the liberating British Army. Jack Ross-Needham had had a good war, but the drab peace of Socialist Britain was not to his liking; he had emigrated to Rhodesia and sunk his entire capital into Hillcrest, which he and his wife had soon built up into a fashionable holiday retreat.

At fifty-six Jack Ross-Needham was still a strong healthy man, only slightly overweight, with a head of thick grey hair parted in the middle, and two prongs of mustache that looked from behind like a pair of buffalo horns; while his wife had conserved her trim figure and a neat, parched prettiness, animated by her smile. They were a happy pair, with a young married daughter and a son in the Security forces, and with no apparent cares beyond the usual economic problems that had nagged everyone in the country for nearly ten years.

The bar over which Ross-Needham presided would have been the envy of any English country pub or club: cosy without being cramped, with dark-stained paneling, plenty of horse brasses and hunting prints, and an impressive collection of beer mats from all over the world, arranged in a mosaic behind the bar. Ross-Needham's favorite was one he had taken himself from an SS officers' mess near Bremen, with the inscription *Blut mit Ehre*. Like many of his guests, the proprietor of Hillcrest was proud of having helped defeat the Teutonic master race.

The two men who had come into the bar were both

middle-aged and deeply sunburned. They were regular visitors to the hotel who came up for three weeks every year for the golf and fishing. One of them was John Campbell, who had caught the four-pound trout that morning. A former RAF fighter pilot, and now an insurance broker, he was one of the few guests who brought his family to Hillcrest. He had married, late in life, a strikingly beautiful girl, who was now upstairs putting their two equally lovely daughters, aged nine and seven, to bed. Campbell was very proud of them and could never resist the chance to show them off, although he was disappointed that so far his wife had not given him a son.

Mrs. Ross-Needham left them to celebrate Campbell's catch, and went through to the kitchen to supervise the supper: tomato soup, braised beef with new potatoes and peas, and a choice of custard pie or fresh fruit.

At exactly 7:30 one of the boys rang the gong at the foot of the stairs. A moment later the guests—men in sports jackets and ties, women in printed frocks and sensible shoes—gathered in the dining room, where the waiters stood in pressed white uniforms around the walls. One of the last to enter was an elderly man with dilapidated good looks and tired eyes behind horn-rimmed spectacles, who took his place alone at a table in the corner. This was the reticent Mr. Fielding, distinguished by the fact that he was the one guest who drank wine with his meals.

Only John Campbell did not go in with the gong. He finished his second drink with Ross-Needham and his friend, then stood at the foot of the stairs and waited for his wife. She came down a couple of minutes later: a honey-skinned beige-blonde who looked no more than twenty, in a white mini-skirt and high-heeled sandals. Campbell watched her long legs moving down toward him and felt a luxurious contentment as he held her around the waist and kissed her mouth. It was the last time he ever did so.

The sound of the gong, carrying clearly through the dusk, was the signal for the boy by the pool to put down his net and return to the hotel. As he did so, a second sound reached him. It came from the valley, muffled by the trees but still recognizable: the grating of gears on a steep turn in the road below. As he started up the lawn he expected the car to appear a moment later from behind the trees that grew up to the hotel forecourt.

But no car appeared. This was odd, because the nearest habitation was eight miles away—a sprawling house called "Nirvana Heights," belonging to an industrialist who lived alone but for four servants and a couple of wolf-hounds. The boy wondered if the car had broken down and whether he should report the fact to Mrs. Ross-Needham. But he did not think long. It was none of his business. He quickened his walk around the back of the hotel, through the shifting pools of mist and darkness and the shrilling of grasshoppers.

The Ross-Needhams always made a point of being the last to enter the dining room. They did so with an air of calculated informality, smiles all round, a word to this table and that, accompanied by a second, synchronized bow from the waiters. Even the isolated Mr. Fielding merited a nod.

This evening Jack Ross-Needham was about to close the bar when he heard the crunch of footsteps on the gravel outside. His face showed mild impatience; it was annoying to have guests arrive just after the gong had sounded, especially if they only wanted a drink. At the same moment his wife appeared, frowning. "Jack, the phone's dead."

"What, dear? Dead?"

"I can't get through. I've been trying the Carters for the last five minutes—about Saturday night—and I can't even get a dial tone." As she spoke the door of the porch slammed shut.

Ross-Needham lifted the hatch in the bar and came through. "That's odd," he said, "there hasn't been a storm. And the lights are all working." He broke off with a forced grin as two men entered. "Evening, gentlemen! The bar's officially closed. Dinner, y'know. But if you could make it a quick one . . ." He did not finish. At the same moment each man pulled an automatic pistol from inside his hunting jacket and shot Mr. and Mrs. Ross-Needham in the stomach. The explosions were simultaneous, and in the enclosed space of the bar they sounded like a small bomb. The silence that followed only emphasized what happened next. Mrs. Ross-Needham collapsed first. Her husband stepped back, struck the open bar hatch, slid under it, and sat down with a thump. Then his wife began to scream. It was an animal sound—not of fear or outrage or even a cry for help, but of pure pain. Her husband lay next to her, and together they rolled about on the floor, hunched, griping, dragging at their bellies—two respectable middle-aged people who had hardly raised their voices in anger since adolescence—now howling and writhing obscenely, impossible to distinguish the man's voice from his wife's.

It continued for five seconds; then both men stepped forward, took aim, and carefully shot the Ross-Needhams through the head. No word was exchanged. They turned and, still holding their guns, walked out of the bar.

When the shots were fired, there were sixteen people in the dining room, including four women, two boys, aged twelve and nine, and three waiters, who were removing the soup course.

The first reaction was silence, as every head turned to the door; and when the screaming started most of them sat rigid, gaping. The two children looked puzzled. Then a couple of men nearest the door—John Campbell and his trout-fishing friend—sprang to their feet. As they did so, the door swung open and three men entered. They spread out along the wall and each lifted a skeleton-handled machine-pistol. The trout fishers hesitated a fraction of a second; and in that moment the two final shots rang out from the bar and the screaming stopped. Both men flung themselves forward, diving low in a concerted rugby tackle, as two bursts of bullets hit each of them in the shoulder, swinging them round and slamming them sideways in opposite directions. Then all three weapons opened up from the wall. The gunmen held them low, from the hip, their left hands resting along the air-cooled muzzles as though to soothe the jumping motion as the barrels scythed from left to right, firing on semiautomatic, aimed a few inches above each table—nine tables in all, three tables a burst.

They fired for six seconds, then broke off the spent magazines and snapped in three fresh ones from the side pockets of their jackets. One of them fired a final, deliberate burst at the corner where Mr. Fielding's head was lolling back against the curtains, his spectacles perched crookedly on the tip of his nose. The bullets hit him in the mouth and throat: his face split open and his head bounced forward onto the table with a clonk like a hollow coconut, upsetting his glass of vin rosé.

Then everything was quiet. From the hi-fi above the door came murmurings from *Funny Girl*. There was a short choking sound; something slithered sideways and a chair scraped back; a glass rolled off a table and shattered on the floor.

One of the two men had appeared from the bar, still carrying his pistol at his side. He nodded at the other three, and began to walk between the tables, noting that the fire had been accurate and economical. Only three window panes had been broken, together with a few glasses, a jug of water, and a bottle of HP sauce, which had splashed messily over Mr. Prentice's bald head. Most of the victims had been shot in the chest or head; and at least three, including the twelve-year-old boy, had taken a bullet between the eyes.

The man with the pistol found it necessary to give only two *coups de grâce*—to John Campbell's friend, who was still stirring by the wall, and to Janice Campbell, who suddenly moaned through a spew of vomit under the table where her husband had pushed her down when the shooting started. The man dispatched each of them with a single shot through the base of the skull.

Meanwhile, more firing had broken out at the back of the hotel, where the cook, the rest of the waiters, and the boys had run out onto the lawn, screaming with terror as they were gunned down rhythmically by three more men, who were waiting under the trees.

The original five, from the bar and dining room, now separated—one taking the kitchen, another two the servants' quarters, and the two from the bar making for the stairs. They moved quickly, but without haste, each taking one wall of bedroom doors. Hillcrest was not the sort of hotel where guests kept their rooms locked. All were empty except one. Here the door had been left ajar. One of the gunmen pushed it open with his foot and a child's voice murmured, "Mummy! Daddy, Mummy!" In the spear of light the man could distinguish two small blond heads staring from above the counterpanes of the twin beds. He paused, then stepped quickly back and closed the door. As he did so, his companion appeared beside him.

"All clear?"

The first man nodded and started back down the corridor, when there came a muffled cry from behind them: "Mummy! *Daddy!*"

Both men stopped. The first one glanced back at the door and shrugged. "Just a couple o' kids," he said.

"Kids be damned," said the other. He walked back and threw open the door.

"Daddy!" both voices cried together, and the man held the door open with one hand and with the other fired two rapid shots, then drew back and closed the door.

The shooting outside the hotel had stopped. Both men walked back without speaking, down the stairs and out onto the forecourt, where they rejoined their companions, who were moving among the rows of cars parked under the wall of the hotel. Two gunmen were distributing wallets, driving licenses, identity cards, and car keys from the pockets of the dead guests, while the others were systematically testing to find which key fitted which car. Five minutes later the first car in a convoy of five—an old Ford Cortina with city plates—backed out into the drive, swung around, and with dipped lights headed slowly down toward the valley. The others followed at intervals of one minute.

Behind them, Hillcrest Hotel lay lit up and silent.

■

The day broke hot and heavy, with storm clouds collecting over Inyanga, where the mountains rolled back across the border into Mozambique.

Down in Umtali, on the broad bed of the valley, the dust was being patted down by the first gobs of rain. At every intersection stood a pair of mixed police—the African with solar topee and truncheon, the European with peaked cap and holstered automatic. Outside Police Headquarters a continuous relay of white Land-Rovers had been coming and going since dawn. Smart young officers in khaki shorts and knee socks hurried up and down the porch steps, saluting the African constables with their canes. Later, auxiliary police and special frontier troops began arriving with rifles and light machine guns; helicopters rattled above the hills; and shortly before noon two armored cars drove through the town.

The news of this latest atrocity had broken just before midnight, when two late arrivals at Hillcrest—a tobacco planter and his wife from Gwelo, whose car had broken down in the bush—had turned up at the hotel to find not a single person, European or African, alive. The husband had driven down to Umtali and reported to the police while his wife was treated at the hospital for shock.

In less than an hour a full state of emergency had been declared on both sides of the border. Roadblocks had been set up as far away as the outskirts of Salisbury, Bulawayo, Fort Victoria, and along the Mozambique frontier. Tracker dogs, native scouts, and several thousand Security troops had been brought in to cover every track and path over an area extending for more than five hundred miles.

Meanwhile, people crowded into Umtali. All morning they had been coming, in a steady stream of cars, double-parking at meter bays without paying or caring, while the African traffic wardens watched nervously from under the arcades, sheltering from the rain.

The first to arrive were local residents—retired farmers and tourists from the other outlying hotels who had heard the news from the first radio bulletins or from friends on the telephone and had hurried into the town for further news, for reassurance, and, above all, for security. Later they began arriving from farther afield, across the border and from the cities to the west: businessmen, tobacco planters, sightseers, relatives of the victims, and reporters. And for once, in this suspicious suburban backwater, the international press was not unwelcome. For these were the boys who could splash the full horror of Hillcrest onto the breakfast tables and TV screens of the world, and teach those complacent liberal critics outside what the struggle down here was all about.

And with the press came the rumors. In the packed terrace café of the Cecil Hotel no theory was too extravagant. The attack was the prelude to a mass uprising by Frelimo, the Mozambique "freedom fighters"; the massacre had been organized by the Chinese; the Chinese had crossed the Zambesi; there were African hordes mobilizing in Zambia, Tanzania, Malawi; while other OAU states were preparing to send volunteers.

The more sober citizens counseled against such alarmist talk; but as the rain fell, and gin and beer flowed, tempers in the hotel began to find expression in noisy opinions about the native population—opinions not usually voiced outside the privacy of one's home. However, beneath the anger of this simple stoic community there was also fear. For the massacre had been executed with a thoroughness that was inconsistent with the sporadic, hit-

and-run terrorist groups who occasionally struck across the border, and could usually be repelled by a resident's rifle. In this case there was not only the efficiency of the attack, but also the extraordinary delay in catching the killers.

Despite the strict secrecy of the operation, it was known that Colonel Bruce Monks, chief of the local Security forces, had taken charge of the hunt. At around mid-morning he was joined by Brigadier Erasmus de Witwe of BOSS, the South African Bureau of State Security, who was deposited by helicopter on the lawn behind Police Headquarters; and shortly afterward a black sedan brought de Witwe's Portuguese counterpart, Senhor Filipo-Munga, a fussy little man with a well-tailored paunch and green-tinted glasses who paused to be photographed before hurrying into the conference which had been going on since dawn.

By lunchtime there was still no official announcement, although Colonel Monks' adjutant, who was well known to the regulars in the Cecil Bar, called in several times for coffee and sandwiches, and dropped odd items of information. These were not encouraging. For some hours it had not been possible to identify all the victims, since the killers not only had stripped the bodies of all personal papers, but also had torn the last two sheets out of the hotel registration book. However, from the adjutant's latest call it was learned that the killers had escaped in at least five stolen cars, three with Salisbury number plates, one from Bulawayo, and one from Durban, in the Republic.

The implications of this news were more ominous than at first appeared.

How could five carloads of armed African terrorists

vanish during the night? Not only had normal police checks on all main roads been doubled, and the paths through the surrounding hills been scoured by dogs, scouts, and helicopters since dawn, but also the Portuguese authorities had mounted their own manhunt on their side of the border. It was some hours before anyone gave voice to the awful possibility that was later to emerge as the truth.

At four o'clock that afternoon Colonel Monks and his two companions held a press conference in the hotel lounge, inviting for good measure a number of leading citizens and local residents, besides the newsmen. Monks' statement was terse and full of false confidence; but after conceding that no trace had yet been found of either the killers, the murder weapons, or the five stolen cars, he announced that the victims of Hillcrest had all—with the exception of the Ross-Needhams—been shot with .30-caliber M-16s, the U.S. Army's light machine-pistol. (He refrained from remarking that until now African terrorists had almost invariably used the Chinese or Russian equivalent, the AK-47.) The Ross-Needhams, on the other hand, had been shot with .38s, the standard caliber of side arm carried by the armies and police forces of White Africa.

On being questioned, Colonel Monks made another disturbing admission. Jack Ross-Needham had been a member of the local Umtali pistol club, and had been a crack shot. Furthermore—one of his friends in the lounge pointed out—he had owned a revolver and a high-velocity rifle; and the revolver he always kept handy under the till in the bar. Yet he and his wife had both been shot in the bar—and in the stomach, not the back—without making any apparent effort to reach either the gun or the alarm system, which was wired to a howler siren and Umtali Police Headquarters. The only precaution that the killers seemed to have taken was to cut the hotel's telephone line.

Colonel Monks drew no conclusions himself, and his South African and Portuguese colleagues were silent. It was left to a senior British journalist to point out that police checks on main roads throughout the country were applied only perfunctorily to Europeans. He also reminded the audience that white Rhodesians, still subjected to gasoline rationing under the Sanctions, made a regular practice of driving over the border into Mozambique and filling up their cars at the nearest pump—which in this case was at Vila de Manica, seven miles inside the border on the road to Beira. Furthermore, cars of Rhodesian registration driven by Europeans were usually ignored by Portuguese patrols.

What was the Englishman suggesting? asked Colonel Monks impatiently.

The journalist replied: "The only solution that fits all the facts as we know them, Colonel, is that the killers could not have been African. They must have been Europeans."

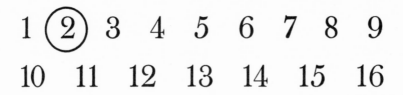

1 ②  3  4  5  6  7  8  9
10  11  12  13  14  15  16

*It began with an item in the diary column of one of London's plumper Sunday newspapers:*

*I hear that my intrepid Antipodean colleague Barry Cayle is thinking of writing a novel about "Kim" Philby—still believed by many to be the greatest spy of all time. Cayle is convinced that the whole story has been far from told.*

*I suggested that as so much has already been written about Philby, is there anything new to say? Cayle thinks there is: "Something the press can't touch because of the Official Secrets Act and the libel laws."*

*Knowing Cayle's reputation as one of Fleet Street's ablest fact-finders, Whitehall will no doubt be among those most eagerly awaiting his first excursion into fiction.*

The day before the paper came out, Cayle left for the Middle East on a trip around the new Arab-Israeli peace lines. On his return three weeks later he found a letter waiting for him at the office from a Mr. Peter Hennison, literary agent. It was dated two days after the diary piece had appeared, and stated that Mr. Hennison was familiar with Barry Cayle's work, and concluded, "I should be most interested to discuss the whole Philby story with you. Perhaps you could ring me and we could meet for lunch?"

Cayle forgot; but when he phoned two days later and gave his name to a secretary, he was put through at once.

Hennison suggested they meet next day at 12:45 at his office in Holborn. He had a pleasant cultured voice, and though not in the least patronizing, there was just a hint to suggest that he did not expect Cayle to refuse. Cayle knew and cared almost nothing about the literary world, and had never heard of Peter Hennison Ltd.; but the address was close to the paper's offices, and since he had nothing else to do for lunch next day, he accepted.

At ten past one he parked his mud-colored Mini-Moke on a yellow line outside a Georgian house overlooking Lincolns Inn Fields. Hennison received him in a handsome room with walls crowded to the ceiling with books —the majority of them in foreign languages. Hennison was sitting in his shirt sleeves on a cluttered desk, swinging a leg and talking on the telephone. He waved Cayle into an armchair and went on talking, in rapid fluent German.

Cayle sat down and tapped out one of his Dutch cheroots, while Hennison, still talking, leaned back across the desk and flicked a lighter at him.

He hung up at last. "Sorry about that. Long distance. Barry Cayle, isn't it? How do you do?" He sprang off the desk and came around with his hand extended. "Glad you could make it!"

He was a slight, rather untidy man with loose grey hair and a faintly donnish manner. Cayle put him in his middle fifties, and guessed that he might have had an interesting war record. He gave Cayle a quick smile. "I won't beat about the bush. Unlike some professions, we literary agents tout for work. I saw you're writing a novel about Philby, and, as I said, I'd like to discuss it with you. No commitments, just a chat. I'm rather interested in Philby myself. I might even be able to help you." He was interrupted by the telephone. "Damn. Just a moment." He lifted the receiver, listened, then told the caller to ring back. "It's no good—we'll never be able to talk here. Let's pop round to the pub."

He pulled on a tweed jacket and led the way out. In the outer office he stopped to tell his secretary—a graceless girl with uneven make-up—to take the names of all callers· and say he'd be back at three o'clock. He grinned as they reached the stairs. "Same old story! Too much work and not enough staff. I need an assistant who speaks at least two languages, besides English. You see, I specialize in foreign rights. Mostly nonfiction. You'd be an exception."

The compliment made Cayle slightly uncomfortable. "I should explain, Mr. Hennison," he said, as they reached the front door, "that I haven't written a word yet. I haven't even got a plot worked out."

"Not to worry, my dear fellow; it's the idea that counts. And I've a suspicion that it's a damned good idea!" He opened the door and strode out into the February cold. Cayle was wearing his Sherpa Tensing parka—a memento from his coverage of the last International Everest Expedition—but Hennison had only his jacket, without even a waistcoat or sweater. They crossed into Lincolns Inn Fields; and although Cayle was a fast walker, and had longer legs than Hennison, he found it difficult to keep up with him.

Hennison talked all the way. He was an easy, skillful talker who made even personal questions seem like casual conversation; and by the time they had crossed the Fields, Cayle had outlined most of his career since coming to London nearly fifteen years ago: how he'd worked first as second string to the crime reporter on a notorious Sunday tabloid, then done free-lance pieces on anything from bird sanctuaries to an Australian bachelor's view of London girls; and later traveled to Beirut, where he'd become an occasional contributor, then full-time correspondent for the paper on which he now worked, rising over the years to be cast as their front-line trouble shooter and general outdoors man: anything from wars and revolutions to climbing Everest and trying his hand in the Transatlantic Solo Yacht Race, in which he'd distinguished himself by being last out of Plymouth and last into Rhode Island. He was now planning to bicycle across the Andes, which had led one wag on the staff to remark that the paper was becoming "an adventure playground for foreign correspondents."

Cayle himself seemed type-cast for this equivocal role. He was a large, loose-limbed man of indeterminate middle age, with broad sloping shoulders, a substantial stomach that was mostly muscle, and a beak-shaped nose which had been broken twice and now resembled the end of a can opener. As always—and often to the dismay of his superiors—he was dressed comfortably, like a man who permanently travels light.

They had left the Fields, and Hennison headed him down some steps into a smoky vault full of sawdust and corpulent men with loud laughs. A waiter in a white apron led them past rows of wine casks to a reserved table in an alcove. Hennison suggested smoked-salmon sandwiches, and after deliberating over the wine list, chose a Puligny-Montrachet, without consulting Cayle.

There was a pause. Hennison folded his hands on the table and smiled. His eyes were the color of weak tea. But deceptively weak, Cayle decided. The man had a brisk, solicitous manner which Cayle instinctively distrusted.

"You said just now you might be able to help me, Mr. Hennison."

"Help you? You mean the book?" The agent's smile brightened. "Yes of course! But allow me first to ask you a question, Barry. The story in your paper seemed to imply that you believe Philby had accomplices."

Cayle grinned. "You don't want to believe everything you read in the papers, Mr. Hennison. But what's the question?"

"Do you think there's still something wrong about the Philby case?"

*"Wrong?* It bloody stinks."

"From a newspaperman's point of view?" said Hennison. "Or a novelist's?"

"From just about any point of view. The whole story doesn't hang together. I've read all the press reports and books on the case, and they add up to asking more questions than they answer." He broke off while the waiter poured some wine for Hennison to taste.

"Are you suggesting, then, that there was an official cover-up in the case?" Hennison said at last, no longer smiling.

"I'm not suggesting it. I'm stating it as a bloody fact. Not only *was* there a cover-up, but it's still going on!" He had Hennison's full attention now. "Three young Englishmen in their early twenties—Guy Burgess, Donald Maclean, and Harold Adrian Russell Philby. All recruited by the Russkies at the same time, back in the thirties, from the same university and the same upper-middle-class background. But the coincidence doesn't stop there. When those three lads get finally rumbled, they all somehow just manage to slip through the net, and next thing we know, they're being given the red carpet in Moscow. In

Kim Philby's case, he got the full treatment, including a top gong—the Order of the Red Banner—plus his head on a bloody postage stamp. There's fame for you!"

"Of course, one must admit," said Hennison, "that a full-dress trial for any one of them would have proved highly embarrassing—particularly in front of our American friends."

"Sure," said Cayle. "And even more so if it had got out that the three of 'em hadn't been acting alone."

"The old canard of the Fourth Man?" Hennison smiled blandly and shook his head. "I feel that story's been around too long. If there'd been anything in it, somebody would surely have exposed it by now."

"Plenty of us have tried," said Cayle. "As you know, my paper was the one that first broke the story back in the late sixties. I was never directly involved in it, but I got talking to the reporters working on it. It wasn't the facts that interested me so much—it was the fantastic efforts made by the British authorities to try to kill the story. You know—those bowler-hatted bods who describe themselves in *Who's Who* as being attached to the Ministry of Defence. Their first line of attack was to treat the whole project as a bad joke, putting it around that Philby had been just a drunken bum of no importance whatever.

"Well, when that didn't pay off, they changed tack and said that Philby had been far *too* important. They tried to warn the editor off on security grounds. They even started a smear campaign, saying that the reporters working on the story were Communist subversives, and that the whole project was just a carefully staged Moscow propaganda stunt. At the same time they let it get around, by whispering in the right ears, in the right clubs, that the bigwigs on the paper's managerial staff could kiss good-bye their CBE's if the story ever got into print.

"But when that didn't work, they started playing rough. First they slapped on the old 'D' notice, which used to be the government's nice way of telling a newspaper to shut up, without actually looking as though they were guilty of censorship. The editor took the unprecedented step of disregarding the notice. But in the end, of course, the usual soggy old British compromise was reached. Whitehall and the Foreign Office were allowed to read all the galleys before they went to press, and cut out anything they didn't like. And when the story finally did appear, it certainly made the British Security Services look pretty bloody silly. But as for containing anything really damaging, all that came out were the unanswered questions. And they're still unanswered."

Hennison inclined his head and smiled at the middle of the table. "I don't want to sound discouraging, Barry. But what you've told me is hardly proof of the kind of conspiracy you've suggested. I'm referring, of course, to the existence of more traitors in the British Establishment."

"So who the hell recruited Comrades Burgess, Maclean, and Philby in the first place?" said Cayle. "Who was able to pick them out all those years ago back at Cambridge? Recognize just the right characteristics, the right weaknesses, the right neuroses and sense of social guilt that all combined to turn three young English gentlemen into lifelong traitors? Whoever that person was—or is—must have one hell of an insight into the British social structure!"

For a moment Hennison's eyes lifted and met Cayle's; and they held in that moment an expression of distinct unease. When he spoke, his words were muted and slightly rushed: "Yes, but you must remember that Communism was very much in vogue in the thirties, particularly among students. A lot of them joined the party, and some of them may even have been introduced to Soviet agents in England who may in turn have tried to recruit them for espionage purposes. How many of them took the final jump we shall probably never know. But my own opinion is that Burgess, Maclean, and Philby were exceptional cases."

Cayle gave him a tired grin. "Oh, they were exceptional, all right, Mr. Hennison! Those three boys were long-term penetration agents. When they signed on, it was for the duration. They gave themselves up, body and soul, to Stalin's Utopia, and stuck to it right through the Terror and the mock trials, the Nazi-Soviet pact and the attack on Finland, when most card-carrying members and fellow-travelers were turning their backs on the CP and searching their hearts like a bunch of guilty schoolgirls.

"Only not Comrades Burgess, Maclean, and Philby. They stayed the course. They stayed as full-time employees of the OGPU and the NKVD, organs of mass murder which didn't think twice about knocking off doubtful foreign agents, even outside Russia. Yet the weird thing is, the Russkies apparently regarded these three British oddballs as reliable—which is pretty strange when you consider that all three were experienced piss artists, and two of them roaring queens! In fact, none of them seems to have had even the first qualification for a job like espionage, where discretion counts pretty high. And you know what they say about a spy in the field? That he's like a test pilot or a professional boxer—after seven years he's burned out. Yet Burgess and Maclean kept at it for twenty years, and Philby for more than thirty! That must have taken one hell of a lot of control." He paused. "Who was that controller, Mr. Hennison?"

Hennison's eyes were again lowered, his features smooth

and colorless. The only trace of emotion was a hand that plucked steadily at the sleeve of his jacket.

"I'm not talking just about the man who first recruited the three of them back in Cambridge," Cayle went on. "I'm talking about the one who 'ran' them. Is he still alive? Still around? Does he have a nice big office in Whitehall and a cushy armchair in White's? And who are his cronies? His associates? His fellow-conspirators who kept quiet for all those years, and were able to kick over the traces when the going got rough?"

Hennison peered up at him now with his weak smile. "Even if there were some truth in your theory, most of the people concerned would be retired by now, or dead."

"I don't think so," said Cayle. "Given the fact that they'd be only a few years older than Philby, they'd be in their sixties or early seventies. And top civil servants are never completely retired. Unlike politicians, there are no voters to kick them out."

"What facts have you got?"

"The facts are gone. Buried. Destroyed by Philby's coconspirators."

"You sound very sure. Have you tried talking to retired members of the FO? Or even old MI6? There are quite a few disgruntled people about who might be prepared to talk—especially with a whisky or two inside them."

Cayle shook his head. "You'd never get near the people who really know the truth. Trying to get a straight answer out of your average British civil servant is about as easy as listening for a snake to fart."

"Have you any particular theory about who this person might be?" Hennison asked slowly.

"My bet is it must have been someone very close to the three of them. Someone who knew and understood each of them perfectly. Someone able to keep them on the rails. A sort of glorified friend—father—schoolmaster—priest—professor. He also had to be someone powerful enough to cover up for them when the crunch came. And in the case of Kim Philby, he even got the whole British Secret Service to cover up! Because one thing's for sure: that 'someone' was no bullet-headed *apparatchik*. Nor was he a dreamy-eyed Lefty from Cambridge. He was—and probably still is—someone on the inside, and very high up. What's more, he almost certainly wasn't alone. It would have needed a full professional team to run a spy network like that. Otherwise, if one accepts your comfortable theory about Burgess, Maclean, and Philby being exceptional cases, they'd have been rumbled long ago."

"They were, finally."

"Yes," said Cayle. "And what happened? They lit out—just as they were supposed to."

Hennison had not moved. Cayle continued: "We know that Philby was the Third Man, who tipped off Burgess and Maclean before they skipped in 1951. But now let's look at what happened to him. In 1962 he was still sunning himself in Beirut as the Middle East correspondent for the *Observer* and the *Economist*—to whom he'd been obligingly recommended by his old chums in the FO. Then suddenly the roof falls in. A high-ranking Polish Intelligence officer defects to the West. The first thing that happens is the arrest of George Blake, who's jailed in London, for forty-two years, before he miraculously escapes.

"Kim must have known that if this Pole could put the finger on Blake, he could do the same to him. So by the end of '62 Kim's deep in the shit. But what does he do about it? Or, more to the point, what do the British do about it? They let him sit in Beirut more or less permanently pissed for the next couple of months, while MI6 sends out one of his old mates to visit him, and they spend hours together in Kim's favorite bars—at the Normandy and St. Georges hotels—trying to soft-talk him into making a nice helpful confession."

"You know all that for a fact?"

Cayle shrugged. "It's the official version—as far as there *is* an official version. You see, Whitehall's theory seems to have been that Kim would be more co-operative in a bar in Beirut than in a cell in Brixton. And if people believe that, they'll believe the Pope's a Jew."

"If I remember rightly," Hennison said, "the details of that Beirut episode are very hazy. You'll pardon my saying so, Barry, but you're in danger of confusing fact with hypothesis."

"One fact I'm damn certain of, Mr. Hennison. Kim Philby stuck around in Beirut for those two months because he was bloody certain that the British didn't dare touch him. Christ! he even made a couple of trips to the Yemen during that period, and, each time, his plane had to land in Aden, which was still a Crown colony, where the British could have picked him up as easily as if he'd been in Piccadilly Circus."

"So what made him finally leave?"

"As I heard it, the Yanks had decided to move in on the job. I know for a fact that the day after he disappeared, on the night of January 23, 1963, the whole of Beirut was swarming with CIA boys, who weren't making any secret of the fact that they'd come to settle his hash once and for all. They had a pretty big score to pay off, remember. Philby had been the chief British liaison officer with the CIA during the height of the Cold War, when he probably did his greatest damage to the Western cause. Washington had clearly rumbled him themselves, and he knew it—perhaps through his old MI6 friend, or perhaps through someone even higher up. Anyway, he skipped out in such a hurry that he didn't even pack or kiss his wife good-bye."

Hennison sat for a moment in silence. When he spoke, it was with a tone of benign patronage. "It might make a good yarn, Barry. But it's an awfully long way from proving your grand-conspiracy theory. The truth, I suspect, is much simpler and much duller. When the authorities knew for certain that Philby was a spy, they probably weighed the pros and cons of the case and decided on balance that, since the damage had already been done, no good could come of a messy trial, even *in camera*. Nobody benefits from a spy scandal—except the newspapers."

"That's right," said Cayle, "and keep the skeletons hidden under the dress shirts. The fact that a few more spies and traitors are still at large in high places doesn't matter, of course?" He shook his head. "I don't know a lot about the details of intelligence work, but I do know that an important part of it is the debriefing of enemy agents. And when that agent turns out to be one of your own boys, it becomes doubly important. In Philby's case, not only would he have been an invaluable source of information to the British and Americans—able to give them all kinds of insight into how Soviet Intelligence had worked during his thirty years with them—but also he was equally invaluable to the Russkies. For them he must have been a walking encyclopedia of how MI6 and the CIA operate—giving them all kinds of details that he could never have got out to them while he was working undercover in the West. So, by letting him go, the British chalked up a double minus. They lost their chance to debrief him themselves, and at the same time handed him to Moscow on a plate."

Hennison finished his smoked salmon and wiped his fingers on a napkin. "You must remember that nothing in intelligence work is ever straightforward. For all you or I know, there may have been quite a number of good reasons why MI6 allowed Philby to leave when he did."

"Sure there were. They wanted to avoid the biggest bleeding scandal in the history of the British Empire!"

"All right. I see no point in arguing about it." There was a tetchiness in Hennison's voice now, while his eyes still held that uncomfortable shifting expression. "I've asked you this already," he added, "and you didn't give me an answer. Do you know the names of any of these so-called fellow-conspirators of Philby's? Or shall I put it another way? Have you ever heard any names mentioned?"

"Without wanting to be rude," said Cayle, "I'd say that question's rather out of court, coming from a literary agent. Particularly as I'm not even your client yet."

Hennison blinked, then lowered his eyes again. "Very well. I understand how you feel. What you journalists call 'confidential sources'? But let me ask you something else. Have you ever had any direct—or even indirect— dealings with Philby?"

"Yeah. I met him."

"Not recently, surely?"

"No, about thirteen years ago, when I was cutting my teeth doing free-lance work in the Middle East. It was in Beirut, just about the time the heat was being turned on him, and he was getting ready to disappear—although I had no idea, of course. I bumped into him only a couple of times. The first was at eleven in the morning in the St. Georges Hotel, and he was sprawled out in his customary fashion, asleep on the bar. I remember the incident because he'd waked up to order a round of drinks. He was just dropping off again when a young man came in and took him under the arm and walked him out to a waiting taxi. Philby seemed so confused he didn't even say cheerio, let alone pay for the round. But the person I remember most was the man he left with. He was British, all right—you couldn't mistake his clothes and accent. Smarmy little bastard with oily eyes. Straight out of the top drawer—obviously not a journalist. He didn't say anything to the rest of us—just gave us a quick once-over, as though we were piles of dog shit. I didn't see him again, but I wouldn't mind laying pretty long odds that he was one of Philby's mates from British Intelligence."

"And the second time?"

"About a week later. We were all being flown on a chartered plane to Aden, then up to San'a in the Yemen. Philby had had a pretty heavy night, and in the morning he wasn't on the bus to the airport. We were sitting in the plane with the engines revving up when a figure came running across the tarmac with a battered old briefcase and just managed to scramble aboard before the steps were taken away. It was Kim. He hadn't shaved and he looked terrible. He took his seat to a standing ovation from the whole press corps."

"A popular chap?"

"Sure. Everybody's favorite drunk."

"Do you remember anything else about him?"

"Only that he kept coming up to us and saying, 'I've just found a little place where they do excellent Abyssinian goat.' "

"How did he get on in the Yemen—it being 'dry'?"

"Didn't seem to worry him at all. That was what struck me most about him. Not only could he turn his drinking on and off like a tap, but also he was amazingly adaptable. He took to the Arab way of life as though he'd always lived there. It was probably hereditary. After all, his father, St. John Philby, had been a great Arabist."

"That mad bastard," Hennison muttered, with surprising venom. "He had a lot to answer for. Like father, like son. Rebels and misfits, both of them. That was the real trouble with Philby—he wanted to fit in and couldn't. But going back to those final months in Beirut, there's one thing you haven't explained. From all I've heard, Philby was obviously cracking up. You said yourself he was drunk most of the time. So if—as you claim—he wasn't frightened of being arrested by the British, what was worrying him? Why didn't he pack his bags and go straight to his beloved Moscow, instead of hanging around risking the vengeance of the Americans, or anyone else who didn't particularly approve of what he'd been doing?"

"My own hunch," said Cayle, "is that once he knew the game was up and realized he'd have to take the jump, he drew back at the last moment. He'd given his whole life to Moscow, but when it came to the point of having to go and live in the bloody place, with no options and no escape, perhaps the prospect wasn't quite so appetizing."

"It's a possibility, knowing Philby's life style. Even if his ideology affected to despise material well-being, he certainly enjoyed his creature comforts. He wasn't a member of the Athenaeum for nothing. And I know that he was very bucked up at getting his CBE."

"Sounds as though you knew him too?" said Cayle.

"I did—quite well, for a time, in a rather humble

capacity during the war. He was stationed with Section Five of the Secret Intelligence Service near St. Albans, and I had a job co-ordinating codes from the Resistance movements. Philby was the man I dealt with."

"How did he strike you?"

"Amiable enough. Lot of charm. Rather schoolboyish sense of humor. Hard drinker and hard worker. And damned conscientious. A good man to work with." He paused. "He was also an A-one copper-bottomed bastard."

"Was that the opinion you formed at the time?" said Cayle. "Or with hindsight?"

"I formed it pretty early on. I've always been on my guard against people with charm, and Philby was very charming. But underneath, there was also something very coarse about him—something that showed in his humor, particularly when he got drunk. He got drunk like an upper-class lout. He was a great suspender-snapper and bottom-pincher, and quite often used to strip down to his underpants and dance on the table—that is, when he wasn't *under* the table."

"Sounds a pretty harmless wartime pursuit," Cayle murmured.

"He was also a thief," said Hennison. "He'd steal anything—reputations, jobs, state secrets, wives, people's affection, trust, loyalty. About the only thing he didn't steal was money. Because Kim Philby was no cheap spy in a dirty mackintosh, selling his country's secrets for a few bundles of fivers. Oh no! He was an idealist—he had a cause. You might even say, a calling. Which perhaps explains that sanctimonious guff that Graham Greene wrote about his having 'a higher loyalty.' Kim Philby had about as much higher loyalty as a black mamba."

"So what attracted him to Communism?"

"Power, and mischief." Hennison leaned forward, his pale eyes showing a slow flicker of enthusiasm. "Look, if you're going to get anywhere trying to understand Philby's true motives, you've got to realize that he wasn't fired by any passion for the working class, which he'd never had anything to do with, or by any real love for Mother Russia, which he'd never been to until he fled there, or even by a belief in Marx, whom I happen to know he found too boring to read. With Philby it was a game. He was like a child at a birthday party who goes around bursting the other children's balloons. He was accepted by the Establishment, and he despised it—he thought he was too good for it. What he really enjoyed was being one up—the snigger in the sleeve as he was entrusted with another top-secret document—stammering his sympathies to the CIA bosses after he had sent a few hundred Albanian exiles to their deaths. He's a ruthless, vain, murderous shit."

"So why were the British so bloody keen to cover up for him?"

Hennison sighed. "Oh dear, we're back to that conspiracy theory again, are we?"

Cayle lit a cheroot and looked steadily at his host, one eye half closed against the smoke. "There's one thing I don't understand about you, Mr. Hennison. You invited me here to talk about a novel I'm thinking of writing. I say a novel, because it seems the likeliest way of getting round the libel laws and the Official Secrets Act. When you originally contacted me, you said you might be able to help me. So far all you've done is tell me that Kim Philby was a bottom-pincher and all-round shit, then throw cold water over my whole idea. What the hell are you after?"

Hennison stared at a point just above Cayle's shoulder. "I'd like to make a suggestion," he said at last. "Why don't you try to see Philby? Sound him out. Perhaps get him over a few vodkas and see if he's prepared to volunteer anything himself about your theory."

Cayle chuckled. "You're not trying to tell me that you'd believe anything he said?"

"I'd certainly be interested to hear what he said."

"Are you offering me a commission?"

"That's something we'd have to discuss. But given your reputation, I don't think it would be too difficult to get a publisher's advance for, say, a travel book about Russia. Certainly enough to cover your expenses. How much do you know about Philby's life in Moscow?" he added.

"We get the odd report from journalists there," said Cayle. "But unlike the old days, Philby keeps well clear of his old mates of the press. Last I heard, he'd had a slight heart attack. Before that, his mistress, Melinda—Donald Maclean's wife—had run out on him and gone back to her hubby, who's supposed to have terminal cancer."

"So Kim's the happy bachelor again?"

"I don't know about happy."

"Oh?" Hennison looked interested. "Why do you say that?"

Cayle grinned. "Have you ever tried living in Moscow?" Hennison did not reply. "Well, you were the one who mentioned his life style. Maybe after thirteen years in the workers' state, the old fellah's getting itchy feet. Might even be thinking of coming back."

Hennison's whole manner fractionally changed; behind the bland composure he had become alert and wary. He said: "Have you any ideas about how you might make contact with Philby?"

"He has an office in the KGB headquarters in Dzerzhinski Square, and he always goes there with at least one bodyguard. If Westerners accost him in the street, he usually answers in Russian and walks on. And nobody's yet tracked down his private address. In other words, it won't be easy."

"You're a resourceful man. You'll find a way. Philby can't be changed all that much. As you say, he must get lonely over there. He likes company, drinks, parties."

"Oh, I can find him all right," said Cayle. "Only there's no guarantee he'll tell me anything. And even if he does, I'm pretty sure it'll be on his terms. But first I've got to get to Moscow."

"That shouldn't present any problems, surely? As I said, you'll go in a professional capacity, paid for by a publisher's advance."

"Now just a minute! Let's get one thing straight, Hennison. I'm not jogging off to the Soviet Union on some subsidized jaunt, posing as a phony novelist or travel-book writer. If I go, I go as the official representative for my paper. I'm too old to spend the next few years carving chessmen somewhere in the Gulag Archipelago."

"I think you're being a trifle melodramatic," Hennison said primly.

"Could be. I'm also touchy about accepting money from strange men."

Hennison seemed unperturbed by this remark. "I appreciate your professional loyalty, Barry. Go for your paper, by all means, if you can persuade them to send you."

"And why shouldn't they send me?"

Hennison gave a delicate shrug. "No reason. But just remember, Philby's poison. To both sides."

Cayle looked at his watch. "Thank you for lunch, Mr.

Hennison. I'll give you a call when I get back from Moscow." He stood up, and was turning away when Hennison called after him.

"Oh, just one thing, Barry! A little tip that might be useful—if you do manage to track Philby down. I'm told he's a great reader, and that he's always glad of books from the West. I'm sure he'd welcome it if you took him one. I suggest something by his old friend and wartime colleague Graham Greene. *The Confidential Agent* might be most appreciated. It's always been his favorite Greene novel. He used to claim that he identified with the hero."

"If it's his favorite, he's probably got it already."

"His English publishers have just issued it in a new uniform edition," Hennison said smoothly. "And Philby's a great collector of new books."

Cayle paused by the table. "You talk as though you were bosom pals." Hennison smiled but said nothing. Cayle went on: "Does it have to be *The Confidential Agent?*"

"Yes. Under the circumstances, it would be very appropriate."

Cayle nodded. "Will you send a copy round to my office?"

Hennison laughed soundlessly and lifted his hand. "All right, I know what you're thinking! Microdots—a code—the first word on every other page." He shook his head, dislodging a shelf of grey hair into his eyes. "No, Barry. You buy it yourself. A brand-new copy, available at all good bookshops. And while you're about it, you might take a couple of cans of cat food. That'll win Philby over completely."

"How do you know he's got a cat?"

"He's got two, as a matter of fact. Not an important

detail, but one never knows when these trifles will come in useful."

"With your sources of information, Mr. Hennison, I should think being a literary agent must get pretty dull." Cayle left him signaling for the check.

When he got back outside Hennison's office, he found his Mini-Moke had collected a ticket.

*"Now, what's all this about taking cat food to* Moscow?" The editor looked past Cayle, out at the sprawl of High Holborn. "I assumed you'd been having a very good lunch. However, you seem to have recovered."

"I was lunching with a bloke called Peter Hennison. Calls himself a literary agent. Know anything about him?"

The editor nodded. "He's sold us a few features and serial rights over the years. What did he want to see you about?"

"Kim Philby. He wants to send me to Moscow to try to talk to Philby, on the pretense that I'm writing a book about Russia. He even offered to pay. I turned him down, of course, and told him that if anyone was going to send me on a junket to the Soviet Union, it would be you."

"I'm flattered. Did he give any reason for choosing you?"

"Just that he'd read that piece about me in the Diary a few weeks back. He seemed bloody interested in my theory about Philby having coconspirators who are still at large. In fact, he spent the first half of lunch trying to talk me out of the idea. But it wasn't that he just didn't believe it. My guess is he not only believes it— he also knows one helluva lot about it!"

"And where does the cat food come in?"

Cayle told him, adding Hennison's "suggestion" about the Graham Greene novel.

"You surprise me about Hennison," the editor said. "The few times I've met him, he's struck me as fairly straight. What's your opinion?"

"I thought there was something fishy about him from the start. Never trust a man who can't look you in the eye. Then it became clear—the man's a straightforward spook. MI5, MI6, DI6, or whatever they call themselves nowadays—friend Hennsion's one of them."

"That's a pretty heavy accusation to make, just because the man doesn't happen to look you in the eye."

"He admitted meeting Philby during the war, when they were both engaged on secret work," said Cayle. "And you know what they say about the Secret Service? It's like the Catholic church and the CP—once you sign up, they never let you go."

"Not necessarily, if it was during the war," said the editor; "otherwise you'd have half the middle-aged dons and journalists and part-time *literati* in Britain still running around playing James Bond's great-uncle."

"Maybe. But Hennison also knows that Philby keeps a couple of cats in Moscow. That's a pretty offbeat piece of information—especially from a London literary agent."

"If I go along with your reasoning," said the editor, "and accept that this man Hennison does work for MI6, then it follows that by telling you about Philby's cats, he was perhaps deliberately dropping you the hint that he's in on the intelligence game. Have you any theories about why he'd do that?"

"My guess is that Hennison and his friends are worried. They're worried that I may know more about this conspiracy theory than I'm letting on. As soon as I mentioned the possibility of Philby having had accomplices who are still at large, Hennison looked distinctly wary. At the same time," he added with a grin, "I think he half took me for the usual dim, hairy-arsed fireman who can be relied on to run a sucker's errand."

"And you didn't disillusion him?"

"Why should I? I've got nothing to lose."

"I wouldn't be too sure about that." The editor stared at him for some time without speaking. "So what do you want to do now?" he said at last.

"I'd like you to send me to Moscow, Godfrey. All nice and aboveboard—fare and expenses paid, and visa applied for through the Foreign Desk."

The editor turned back to the window. "What do you hope to get out of such a trip?"

"Hennison's no fool, Godfrey. He may have misjudged me a little, but I won't hold that against him. He's got a good reason for wanting me to go to Moscow and contact Philby. And providing there's a new angle, Philby's still news—isn't he?"

"That would depend on the angle," said the editor. "I'm not sure I like it, Barry. You know my rule about staff men doubling up with Whitehall—let alone MI6. Well, it applies to you, too."

There was a long pause. Cayle smoked another cheroot and gazed at the ceiling. Finally the editor spoke. "Were the book and the cat food the only things he asked you to take in for Philby?"

"He didn't exactly *ask* me. It was more in the way of a suggestion. Rather like Red Cross parcels during the war."

The editor put his hands on the desk top and stood up. "I'll think about it, Barry."

Aeroflot's midday flight from London to Moscow via Copenhagen left only an hour late. Two-thirds of the four-engined Tupolov had been gutted to make room for cargo cases, which were covered with tarpaulins. The passengers sat at the front. They were all men, mostly Russians in greatcoats and astrakhan hats, whom Cayle put down as diplomats or heads of trade missions. The only one he couldn't place was a short redheaded man in a hairy tweed jacket and a purple shirt that showed too much cuff. He hardly looked like the ordinary Soviet citizen, though Cayle had heard him speak several times to the stewardess in what sounded like fluent Russian. He now sat with an attaché case open on his lap and was scribbling rapidly with a gold pen.

The stewardess, who looked comically like a wardress, ordered them, in Russian and English, to fasten their seat belts and extinguish all cigarettes. She then strode down the aisle and forcibly removed cigarettes from the unsuspecting passengers' mouths, several of whom gave cries of pain as flecks of skin were torn from their lips; but they made no complaint. A moment later the steward appeared, carrying a whole tray of cigarettes, of English and Russian brands, which he proceeded unsmilingly to offer. Cayle sighed contentedly; even before they'd taken off, he felt already close to Russia.

He was unable to fasten his seat belt, since the buckle was missing, so he knotted it instead. Eventually the pilot came aboard, sucking an orange; and a few minutes later they took off. The stewardess came around again, this time with chocolates, beakers of wine, and mugs of *kvas,* an insipid grey liquid made from bread and known as "Russian Coca-Cola." Cayle's beaker was replenished at generous intervals, and he soon dozed off.

He woke to feel his legs numb with cold. The other passengers, including the red-haired man across the aisle, were again wearing their overcoats. Cayle pulled his anorak down from the rack, but it did not reach below his thighs. He eventually attracted the stewardess and asked for a blanket. "It is being used," she replied stiffly. Someone gave a harsh laugh; it was the red-haired man.

"Bloody typical! I know some people who only travel on this line with a hot-water bottle." He was leaning over toward Cayle. "Mind if I join you?" Before Cayle could reply, he had slipped across the aisle and dropped into the seat beside him. "Going to Moscow? Or stopping in Denmark?"

"Moscow," Cayle said, without enthusiasm. He had had a late night and was hoping to get some sleep on the plane. Besides, the stranger's appearance was not prepossessing. He was about forty, with a low forehead, sharp predatory features, and a slight inflation around his nose and his mouth, as though he suffered from a permanent cold. His red hair was tough and wiry, and reminded Cayle of rusted iron wool.

"That's great! We're going there together." The little man held out his hand; it was small, but gave Cayle's a bone-cracking squeeze. "Maddox is the name. Leonard Maddox."

"Barry Cayle."

"Glad to meet you, Barry." He paused, then turned, grinning like a dog. "Barry Cayle," he repeated. "I know that name from somewhere. I'm certain I do!" He snapped his fingers. "Don't tell me—I'll get it in a jiff. That's it—you're a writer. Newspapers—the telly." Maddox stretched his neck, showing a rim of acne under his collar. "Not that I get much time to read the papers, mind—'cept the financial pages. And in Moscow, o' course, it's just the *Morning Star*. But I've always been interested to meet you journalist chaps. Never know when you might pick up something useful."

Cayle felt that this was somehow his cue, but deliberately ignored it. He did not like this turn of the conversation. For a start, he was fairly modest about his status, and was always surprised when he was recognized by people outside the profession. Besides, on his own admission, Maddox didn't read newspapers; and apart from a BBC film of his ill-fated transatlantic yachting expedition, Cayle had scarcely appeared on television.

Maddox went on: "Going to Moscow on business, or pleasure?" He laughed. "Silly question, I know. A good journalist's always on business. Like policemen—always on duty."

Cayle again declined the cue. Instead he said: "And you, Mr. Maddox?"

"Business, o' course! You don't get me holed up in a dump like Moscow unless there's something in it for Lennie Maddox. And I don't mean women. In Moscow that's a dead loss—unless you don't mind sharing your bed with Galina Borisovna." He caught Cayle's eye and leered. "KGB, old boy. Never refer to the outfit by its real name. Here, take this." He snatched a card out of his top pocket and handed it to Cayle. One side was printed in English, the other in Cyrillic. Cayle read:

LEONARD E. MADDOX AMA
*Entreprises Lipp* SA
*5, Quai du Mont-Blanc*
*Genève*

*Room 1727*
*Hotel Intourist*
*Pushkin St.*
*Moscow 1,* USSR

He started to hand it back, but Maddox waved it away. "What line of business are you in, Mr. Maddox?"

"Money." Maddox gave his canine grin. "Money, money, money! You'd be surprised—the Russians are just as keen on it as the next man. Once you've hacked your way through all the red tape, and made them sign on the dotted line, you've got a deal. Ever heard of a Russian welshing? They'd get bloody shot if they did!"

"You spend a lot of time in the Soviet Union?" said Cayle.

"On and off. Not a bad country, once you get used to it. The great thing about the Russian people is they've got no *side* to them. They accept you for what you are. That's what's wrong with Britain—everyone bangs on about free enterprise and opportunities for all, but when it comes to the crunch, what still matters is what bloody accent you've got and whether you wear the right tie." He paused. "I've got a little confession to make to you, Barry. That card I just gave you, it tells a bit of a fib. Those initials after my name—AMA, short for Association of Management Accountants—well, I used to be a member, see, but I got struck off. No skin off my nose, mind! I was just too good at my job. Fixed a beautiful tax dodge for a property company I was working for, only the Revenue boys didn't like it and they started to lean on me. Always the same— show a bit o' gumption in Britain today and they squeeze you out—unless, o' course, you belong to the right club." He inclined his head, grinning for approval; and when Cayle said nothing, he went on.

"With Lipp Enterprises you don't get any of that crap. We're a big international company, dealing in big money."

"What's your exact tie with the Soviet Union?" asked Cayle.

"More or less anything that comes along, old boy. This time it's an aircraft deal. The boss is flying in from

Geneva soon to supervise it. French chappie—great character. One of the fattest sods you ever saw! Can't be more than five foot two, and weighs at least two hundred twenty-five pounds. Should be in a bloody circus!"

"Is it a private deal," said Cayle, "or does he represent the French government?"

Maddox jerked his chin up and gave a crafty smile. "To be frank with you, Barry, I shouldn't really be telling you this. It's a bit hush-hush, y'see. This French boss o' mine has a concession to flog the Russians some aircraft—stocking up the old Aeroflot junk, some of which is nearly twenty years old. But he's also arranged a special new deal with them—a Franco-Soviet airbus. They're calling it the Troika-Caravelle. And it's likely to cause a lot of agro in the EEC."

Cayle nodded. He wondered if Maddox was merely shooting a line, or whether he was being extraordinarily indiscreet. It seemed hardly credible that this unprepossessing little man should be privy to an international secret; and even if he was, why was he blurting it out to a journalist whom he'd only just met, and who was himself traveling to the Soviet Union, where the deal was presumably to be clinched?

Cayle was not a suspicious man by nature, but his profession had trained him to be wary of importuning strangers. He considered the possibility that Lennie Maddox was giving him this information for a purpose.

He said: "Do you work for this Frenchman personally?"

"I do. And what a lovely man to work for. Never entertains without the champagne and caviar. Rich as Croesus —bloody great place on Lake Geneva, travels like a prince, always the best hotels, servants fetching and carrying wherever he goes—and yet he calls himself an international socialist! God knows what the Russians really make of him. But he certainly seems to get his way with them—perhaps because they've never met anybody like him before."

"When do you say he's arriving in Moscow?"

"Next week, next month. You never know for certain with old Charlie boy."

"What's his full name?"

"Pol. Charles Pol, president and chief shareholder of Entreprises Lipp, and the biggest left-wing capitalist from the Kremlin to Wall Street."

"I'd like to meet him," said Cayle.

"Ah. Might be tricky. Don't know that he's too keen on the press—not unless he's got something special to tell them." He finished his wine and put his seat back. "Well, must get a bit o' shut-eye now. Nice talking to you, Barry!"

His interest in their conversation seemed to cease as abruptly as it began, and after the forty-minute stop at Copenhagen, Maddox returned to his seat and went back to the work in his attaché case.

They landed at Moscow's Sheremetyevo Airport at seven o'clock local time. It was a black misty evening, with the runway covered with freezing slush. Inside the terminal they were bunched into a bleak concrete hall, filled with the smell of Russia—the bittersweet fumes of Soviet gasoline, black tobacco, and a hint of cheap soap. A woman with henna-stained hair handed Cayle a pink Customs form warning of severe penalties for importing firearms, explosives, drugs, livestock, undeclared rubles, Western newspapers and magazines, and literature hostile to the Soviet Union; and a young Customs officer, in a square-shouldered greatcoat reaching over the top of his calfskin boots, politely examined his luggage. He looked through the new Bodley Head edition of Graham Greene's

*The Confidential Agent*—bought the day before at John Sandoe's, off the King's Road—but ignored the two cans of Whiskas, from Cayle's local supermarket in Fulham.

Maddox had a car waiting for him outside, but pointedly failed to offer Cayle a lift. However, before driving off he asked him where he was staying.

"The Metropol," Cayle replied reluctantly.

"I'll call you, Barry. We must get together and have a night out." He waved as the car drove off leaving a wake of slush.

There seemed to be no airport bus, only official limousines. Eventually Cayle found a taxi, and they pulled out into the dark suburbs of the Russian capital.

Like the desert, the sense of adventure on entering Russia is soon dissipated by its vast, sterile emptiness. Cayle felt at once cut off from all spiritual and emotional contact, and was left not so much depressed as crushed and listless. They reached the Leningrad Prospekt, a six-lane highway bordered by apartment blocks like rows of tombstones: then the blaze of light as they approached the city center, beneath the wonders of Stalinist Gothic with its soapstone maidens embracing giant sheaves of corn and concrete workers carrying cogwheels the size of houses.

The Metropol loomed out of the night like a well-lit factory. An ancient porter carried Cayle's cases through the revolving doors, into a high-vaulted lobby like the entrance to a railway station, full of liverish marble and crowds in steaming, dripping fur. The Intourist reception desk was along the far wall, where long queues were waiting to have their passports checked, in return for coupon vouchers and numbered passes to their rooms.

Half an hour later Cayle had cleared the formalities and entered an elevator that was already occupied by a large drunken man in a double-breasted suit. Cayle rode up to the third floor, showed his pass to the matron at the floor desk, waited while she selected his key, then walked down several hundred yards of balding carpet to Room 246. It was small and very hot inside. His suitcase was already standing behind the door. He took out his bottle of duty-free Scotch and went into the tiny bathroom to get a glass, but there wasn't one; nor was there any soap or plug for the bathtub. The only consolation was a brand-new roll of toilet paper.

He decided to return downstairs and have a drink at the foreign-currency bar. When the elevator arrived, he stepped in and collided with the well-dressed drunk who had ridden up with him. They stopped at the ground floor, and Cayle stood aside to let him out, but the man stood squinting at the floor, waiting for the doors to close again. Cayle had long accustomed himself to accept the fact that nothing in Russia is quite what it seems to be; and he did not rule out the possibility that the drunk was a security man.

In the bar he paid for his whisky with a pound note and received a Czech crown and two Kenyan shillings in change; then sat inspecting the other guests. There was a delegation of East Germans with lapels studded with party badges; a couple of Africans morosely sipping beer; a row of Western businessmen laughing and tapping their feet to a noisy number by the Rolling Stones. He recognized no obvious Russians.

After half an hour he left for the huge dining room, where he ate alone to the strains of an orchestra of old men in evening dress ravaging Cole Porter under triple chandeliers.

He woke late and had breakfast in his room, then spent some time on the telephone trying to negotiate for some soap and a plug for the bath. When he finally got down-stairs it was lunchtime, but the restaurant was full of old women with mops and vacuum cleaners.

On his way through the lobby he stopped at a desk selling newspapers; there were two racks, one full of the Soviet and East European press, the other with yesterday's Western Communist papers. He asked what time today's papers arrived from the West and was told between three and four o'clock. He knew that the *Morning Star* would be the only English one to be exhibited, but that the big international hotels usually kept a few copies of the London *Times,* along with the *Herald Tribune* and *Le Monde,* available on demand to Western guests.

He looked at his watch: he had between three and four hours to kill. He went outside and took a taxi to an Uzbek restaurant not well known to tourists. There was a long queue inside the door, but he was soon recognized as a foreigner and shown to a table where two men were eating curds with their fingers. Nearly an hour later his food came, tepid and highly spiced, and while he was eating it a young man in a blue suit approached him with an offer in English to sell rubles for dollars. Cayle knew this was one of the oldest tricks for compromising foreign visitors, and said something in broken Russian that made the young man walk hurriedly out of the restaurant. But Cayle was puzzled that he should be so readily conspicuous as a Westerner. He had never enjoyed a reputation for sartorial elegance, and his general demeanor had a markedly proletarian aspect—what a friend had described as a middle-brow lumberjack with a hang-over.

When he returned to the Metropol, it was nearly four o'clock. Today's Western Communist papers were still not on display; but he decided to follow through with his plan all the same. He went to his room and collected *The Confidential Agent,* then took a taxi to the Foreign Post Office in Kirov Street. It was a fifteen-minute drive into a forlorn district full of concrete blocks and broken pavements.

There was a militiaman on the steps of the Post Office who eyed him dolefully as he walked past, into a bright naked hall with queues waiting at the rows of iron grilles. A second militiaman stood at the far end, near the *poste restante.*

The digital clock on the wall said 4:37. Cayle sat down on a bench, tapped out a cheroot and began to light it, when the militiaman yelled at him and pointed at a notice forbidding smoking in four languages. Cayle put the pack away and stared at the crowds. Most of the people looked like students: a lot of Africans and Arabs and Indians, and a few Westerners, who he guessed had been traveling in the Soviet Union and were returning to collect their mail.

The minutes passed slowly. At 4:58 a bell began to ring. There was a clang as the doors were opened. Cayle stood up and passed two men in bulky overcoats and fur hats coming away from the *poste restante.* One of them had a copy of the *Times* in an airmail wrapper tucked under his arm. Cayle stepped up beside him and said, "Excuse me—Mr. Philby?"

A leaky blue eye peered around at him out of a pouchy face, and the man muttered something in Russian and walked on.

Cayle caught up with him again and said, "We met twelve years ago on a trip to Yemen. Nine days without a drink."

The man hesitated, then spoke again in Russian, and his companion took hold of Cayle's arm. With his free hand Cayle produced *The Confidential Agent* from inside his anorak. "I was asked by a friend to bring you this." A second bell rang and the militiaman shouted something from the door. The hall was emptying fast.

"Wh-who are you?"

Cayle told him.

"Wh-where are you st-staying?" he asked, wincing with the stutter. He was shorter and plumper than Cayle remembered, and smelled strongly of Russian cigarettes.

Cayle said, "The Metropol—Room 246."

"I'll c-c-call you." He took the book from Cayle's hand and walked briskly away toward the entrance. His companion waited a full ten seconds before letting go of Cayle's arm, then also hurried off to join the last of the crowd shuffling through the doors. Cayle got outside in time to see the two of them get into a black Volga, which accelerated away with a growl of snow tires.

Cayle was in good spirits. It had been an inspired shot in the dark: the Second Cricket Test Match was being played in the West Indies, and he knew that one of Philby's great passions was to follow the score each day in the *Times*. He no doubt felt that it would offend against protocol to have the paper delivered to his office in Dzerzhinski Square, and to have had it sent direct to his flat would have meant revealing his address to London.

Meanwhile, Philby knew Cayle's hotel and room number; and there was nothing to do but wait.

He was getting into the bath that evening when the telephone rang.

"Barry? How's things?"

Cayle scowled. "Hello, Lennie. And how's the wheeling and dealing?"

"Marking time, old boy. The Frenchie's delayed in Switzerland and it looks as if I've got to cool my heels for a few days. How 'bout a drinkie?"

Cayle had no wish to spend the evening with Leonard Maddox; but there was something about the events of the past twenty-four hours that suggested that his meeting with the man had not been entirely fortuitous. "Where are you?"

"At the office—Hotel Intourist, just across the way. I can be with you in a couple o' shakes. Downstairs bar—all right?"

"All right," said Cayle, and hung up.

He didn't hurry. Half an hour later he found Lennie Maddox waiting patiently in a dark corner of the foreign-currency bar, under a blaring loudspeaker. Maddox waved at him and mouthed wordlessly into the music. No need to worry about "bugs," Cayle thought, as he sat down; and wondered if Maddox had chosen the spot on purpose.

"Enjoying yerself?" Maddox shouted, pushing his face close to Cayle's to make himself heard.

"Does anyone enjoy himself in Moscow?" said Cayle; and Maddox's lips drew back in a soundless laugh.

"Well, there are ways! But then, o' course, you're here to work? Must be a damned tricky place, Moscow, for a journalist. I mean, if you stumble on a really good story, the chances are a ninety-nine per cent cert it's something hush-hush?"

"Like the aircraft deal you and your French boss are pulling off?"

Maddox had turned and was energetically ordering two

double whiskies. "No, I wasn't exactly thinking of that," he said; then cocked his head sideways and put a hand on Cayle's arm. "Know what I think, Barry? I think you're onto a story already."

"And what would that be?"

Maddox squeezed his arm, and his fingers felt very hard. "Don't think me nosy, but a chap like you would hardly come all the way to Moscow just to go to the Bolshoi. So what's the game?"

"I like to live dangerously, Lennie. I like to sit in dark corners and watch nasty things crawl out from under the carpet."

Maddox gulped his drink. "You're not referring to me, are you?" And Cayle noticed that the man's fingers had clenched into a fist.

"I've got no opinions about you, Lennie. And no illusions either. I know you're after something. You picked me up on the plane yesterday and now you're wetting your pants to find out what I'm doing in Moscow."

Maddox had tilted his head back and was stroking his acne-raw neck. "Tell you what," he said suddenly, "how about a bit o' nosh? There's a very good joint round the corner—place called the Ararat. Just the right atmosphere for a friendly chat." He stood up and started toward the door. Cayle followed without protest. As he had said, Maddox was after something, and Cayle felt professionally bound to find out what it was.

The restaurant was fairly crowded, but the waiter found them a table under a crude mural of Mount Ararat, with its twin peaks rising out of a wreath of cloud. The same image was printed in white on the front and back of the waiters' blue T shirts. Maddox insisted on doing the ordering, which included blinis, shashlik, raw herrings, and Caucasian red wine. He was odiously cheerful and talked incessantly. By the second course he was happily laying into Britain again, describing it as a nation of snobs and parasites, and seemed to assume that Cayle, as an Australian, was in full agreement.

"I'll tell you something, Barry," he was saying as the waiter cleared away the shashlik, "in some ways I wouldn't mind settling here. A lot o' people have done it—and some pretty funny ones at that. Westerners, I mean. You know what they call 'em here? They call 'em the 'Grey Men'—because they live in a kind o' limbo, neither Western nor Russian. Most of 'em are fellow-travelers from way back before the war—the ones who somehow escaped the purges and managed to find themselves cosy jobs here, usually with Radio Moscow or the Foreign Languages Publishing House. Nowadays they're mostly too old to go back to their own countries, even if their countries would have them. They couldn't get jobs, for a start—at least, nothing like as well paid as they've got here."

"Look," said Cayle, "I'm not a bloody bitch in heat! Stop sniffing around and come to the point. All this about you wanting to settle down here's a load of balls. Unless, of course, your job with the rich French Marxist's turning sour?"

"What makes you think that?" Maddox said quickly.

Cayle grinned, as the waiter arrived with a multicolored ice cream concoction which he began to slice up onto separate plates, while a second waiter poured brandy over each helping. "Spit it out, Lennie. You were telling me about these so-called Grey Men, and how they can't go back to their own countries. And some can't more than others, eh?"

Maddox took his fork and made a careful incision in the ice cream. He was a fussy eater, one of those who wipe their lips after every mouthful. "You know about my boss—the Frenchman, Pol? Well, he's a pretty big wheel, even out here. Got his finger in a lot o' pies, and I don't just mean the aero industry. That deal with the Troika-Caravelle airbus will be just chicken feed to him. I happen to know, Barry, that Pol's onto something much bigger. Something of international importance."

"Something to do with one of these Grey Men?"

Maddox sat back and grinned nervously. "Could be."

"What's the price, Lennie?"

Maddox paused to let the ice cream melt in his mouth. "Five grand, U.S. dollars—cash, with one grand in advance."

"In advance of what?"

"Giving you a piece of info that'll make headlines round the world."

"According to you. But you're not in the newspaper business. And I'm not in a position to make blind deals with strangers who pick me up in foreign hotel bars."

"Oh, don't be bloody-minded, Cayle! I know a good story when I see one. And even if you don't want it, plenty of others will." He had clenched his fist again and his face had taken on a greyish pallor that exaggerated the inflamed blotches around his nose and mouth. "Don't you even want to hear what the story is?"

"Only if it's free."

"Supposing I told you there was an embassy angle?"

"Depends which embassy," said Cayle.

"Her Majesty's. One of the dips—works in Chancery—anonymous desk job, with a hot line to the nabobs back in Whitehall."

"So?"

"It just so happens," said Maddox, "that he's been having contacts with my boss, Pol. And Pol's been getting very matey with a certain Englishman out here. You might say, the most famous—or, rather, notorious—of all the Grey Men."

"Okay. Kim Philby." Cayle looked hard at Lennie Maddox, who tried to avoid his gaze, shifting in his chair and glancing around for a waiter. "What's your source?"

Maddox smirked, "Secrets of the trade, old boy. Just let's say that as far as Lipp Enterprises is concerned, I may not be a senior partner yet, but I'm not the office boy either. I keep my eyes and ears wide open."

"As well as the occasional piece of private correspondence, no doubt?"

"Now, now! That's not very nice—not from someone you're going to do business with."

"You're jumping the gun, Lennie. I haven't agreed to do any business with you."

"It's cheap at the price!" Maddox cried. "But if your paper's so bloody high and mighty they daren't tread on any precious embassy toes, I'll flog it to one o' the tabloids. They might even make it ten grand."

"So why don't you?"

Maddox paused. "Because your paper was the one that broke the original story. I reckoned you'd be the natural choice."

"That's not the whole reason, Lennie. You're also in a hurry. Maybe something you read in one of the confidential letters to your boss was a bit too hot, even for you? Now you're trying to make a quick thousand bucks, then run for it."

Maddox had turned dark pink and his fists began to shake. "Sod you, Cayle! I've already told you more than's good for either of us. Now you just spit in my face."

Cayle shrugged. "I want names. Sources. Proof."

Maddox dug a fingernail into the tablecloth. "Ever heard of a chap called Hann? Simon Hann, member of Her Majesty's Diplomatic Corps?"

Cayle shook his head.

"Toffee-nosed little bastard. Typical FO—you'd think he spent most of his life dressing."

"What of him?"

"He's been in Moscow for just six weeks. And I happen to know that his real job is connected with Security. A month ago my boss had a hush-hush meeting with him—up in a dacha in the Lenin Hills. Afterward, Pol went straight back to Geneva and I was left more or less in charge of the Moscow end o' the business."

"What are you trying to sell, Lennie?"

Maddox looked anxiously around again for the waiter. "Listen, Cayle." He was sweating now. "Something big is blowing up—and it's to do with Philby."

"Where's the proof?"

"For Christ's sake, I'm not bloody daft! You don't think I keep copies o' those letters, do you?"

"Not if you hadn't planned this thing from the beginning."

"And what the hell does that mean?"

"What I said just now. You've been working with this man Pol on a few fast deals and suddenly you're into something where you're out of your depth. You want to cut your losses, make a quick grand, and run. Right?"

The waiter poured them two brandies, and Maddox swallowed his in a gulp. "Make it five hundred," he said hoarsely. "I can't go lower."

"Sorry. As I said, I'm not empowered to make deals without higher authority. But it would make it a lot easier if you told me just where Philby fits in. What's his connection with this fellow Hann and your boss, Pol?"

"That's what you'll have to pay for. But I can tell you the three of them are in on something together."

Cayle shook his head. "It's not good enough, Lennie. Unless, of course, I could talk to Pol direct and confirm the story with him."

"And get me done in?" Maddox snapped. There was a pause. "I might be able to get something for you," he added. "When Pol gets back. Something in writing, maybe. Or even a photograph." His face now had a pinched, miserable look; he tried to smile. "A photo of Philby meeting Pol—how 'bout that? But o' course, it would mean a bonus."

Cayle took out his wallet and put ten one-ruble notes, which he'd changed at the Intourist desk, in front of Maddox's empty ice-cream plate. "Thanks for the dinner, Lennie. But you're going to have to work a lot harder, even for five hundred dollars." He heard Maddox shout something after him as he collected his anorak from the old woman at the door; but he got outside without any-one following him.

He took a deep icy breath and began to walk quickly away.

At nine-thirty next morning, while Cayle was on his third coffee in his room, the phone rang. He lifted it and heard a croak: "Ck . . . Ck . . . Ck . . ." Then the line went dead and he hung up. It rang thirty seconds later, and the same sound came again.

"Hello," said Cayle. "Hello!"

"Ck . . . Ck . . . Ck . . ." Then again a click and silence.

He returned to his coffee, marveling at a political system where telephones were tapped as a matter of routine, when half of them failed to work.

A couple of minutes later it went again. He let it go on ringing for several seconds before lifting the receiver, and then without answering.

"C . . . C . . . Cayle? B . . . Barry Cayle?"

"Speaking."

"Ph-Philby here. C-c-can you m-meet me this m-morning? Got a p-pen?"

Cayle grabbed one out of his jacket. "Right!" he shouted into the receiver.

"N-number 18 Dimitrievskaya Street, top floor, R-room 648. Got it? F-fine! S-see you at ten-thirty this morning."

Cayle consulted the Moscow street map which he'd bought in London—their being unobtainable in Russia—and found Dimitrievskaya Street leading off the river south of the Kremlin, just beyond the open-air swimming pool.

He finished his breakfast, armed himself with notebook and press cards, and stuffed both cans of Whiskas into the side pockets of his anorak. Outside, it was a pale dry day with a yellow sun hanging low over the skyline and bone-chillingly cold. His face was stiff even before he reached the taxi rank at the corner of the hotel.

The driver already had the engine running and the heater on. They started off, across Red Square, with its long queue shuffling like a black centipede into the Lenin Mausoleum; past the dark-red walls of the Kremlin and the twisted baubles of St. Basil's Cathedral, down to the river, where lumps of brown ice bumped together like basking whales

Dimitrievskaya Street consisted of two rows of featureless apartment blocks, each with a few naked saplings growing out of the frozen earth at its base. Number 18 had a low open doorway with concrete steps leading up into a dark passage where a scarred old man in a muffler and overcoat sat in a concierge's lodge behind a window with two broken panes. Cayle walked past him to the elevator, pushed the top button, and clanked slowly upward. The door opened and he stepped up against a short square man in a long coat and a flat cloth cap that was too small for him. He gave Cayle a dull stare, then turned and nodded toward a carpetless corridor lit by low-powered bulbs in wire cages. There were about half a dozen doors along each wall. At the end stood a second man, in an identical overcoat, but this time with a low-brimmed black fedora pulled down over his eyes.

The doors were of brown flush wood with the numbers stenciled in grey; 648 was about halfway down. Cayle knocked, and the door was opened at once, although he saw no one inside. He stepped through and found himself in what appeared to be an empty room.

The walls were bare and blotched with damp. There was a small double-glazed window, the outer panes grimy with frost. The only furniture was two deal chairs and a wooden table on which stood a couple of glasses and a liter bottle of vodka.

"G-good morning, Mr. Cayle."

Cayle swung around. As he did so the door softly closed. Philby was standing behind it, where he had remained hidden when Cayle entered. "Sit d-down, w-won't you? M-make yourself at home." He stepped forward and nodded at the two chairs. "I apologize for the decor, but it has been r-rather short notice."

He was wearing a dark woolen shirt without a tie and a

lumpy grey suit with leather patches on the elbows. The only item that might have betrayed him as a Westerner was a pair of thick-soled shiny suède chukka boots stained white with salt from the snow. In his left hand he carried a briefcase with the flap open.

He stopped a few feet from Cayle and added: "I haven't the f-faintest idea who you are. But I must w-warn you. If you t-try anything, you won't get as far as the elevator."

Cayle stared at him, trying not to smile. "For Christ's sake, Mr. Philby, I'm only a poor bloody journalist trying to do a job."

"Are you?" Philby gave a small deprecating smile, then he lifted the flap of his briefcase and took out an automatic, which he stood holding on his outstretched palm. To Cayle's practiced eye it looked freshly oiled, but not new.

He said: "I don't want to get shot reaching for my pockets, but I've something to give you."

"You g-gave me something yesterday afternoon."

"I know, but that was by way of introduction. These are for your pussycats." He pulled the two cans of Whiskas from his anorak pocket and put them on the table next to the vodka bottle.

Philby stared at him for a moment, then dropped the gun back into the briefcase and laid it down against the table leg. "Let's have a d-drink. It's not too early for you, is it?"

"Is it ever too early in Moscow?" said Cayle.

Philby sat down and began unpeeling the foil from the top of the bottle. Cayle noticed that it was Osoboya vodka, which has no cork and is meant to be drunk at a sitting. He watched Philby fill both glasses to the brim, raise his in a faint gesture, and swallow it straight. Cayle did the same. There was an awkward pause, interrupted by a clanking and grinding of plumbing. When it had partially subsided, Philby nodded toward the window.

"A b-beautiful city, d-don't you think?"

"Well, it's different, certainly."

"It's not your f-first visit, then?"

"I was here once before—two years ago, for one of those abortive disarmament conferences."

"It's a city that takes a b-bit of getting used to," said Philby, and refilled their glasses. "Not everyone's cup of tea, no doubt. But not all of us in life have the choice."

"A lot of people would say that you'd had more of a choice than most of us, Mr. Philby."

Philby took a sip of vodka and laid his glass carefully down in front of him. His face had tightened: there was a set downward expression about the jaw and the corners of his mouth that was hard, almost brutal. "You're not British, are you, Cayle? I mean, English."

"Australian."

"Ah." Philby sat rubbing his broad fleshy nose. "At first I thought you might be one of those bloody Yanks! They're always over here, trying to get me into a corner and screw me. It's a funny thing," he added, taking a gulp of vodka, "but the British have never seemed to mind me so much. It's the Yanks who've always hated me. You spend your life running rings round the good old British Establishment, and afterward the blighters just don't want to know. But take a crack at the Great Western Alliance, and you're a marked man for life."

"Have you any idea why Whitehall washed their hands of you so easily?" said Cayle.

Philby was about to speak when he was interrupted by another burst of gurgling and groaning from behind the walls. While it was still going on, Cayle said, almost in a shout: "I suppose this place is bugged?"

"You suppose right, Mr. Cayle. And I'll tell you something else—I'm the man who edits the tapes."

"So we can talk freely?"

"That depends what about. About you, for instance. Your background, interests, how you got into this r-racket in the first place."

"You mean journalism?"

Philby gave a loose laugh. "Well, it certainly wouldn't be the first time that Whitehall or the CIA has used innocent newspapermen as errand boys."

"Hence the gun?"

Philby drained his glass. A quarter of the bottle had already disappeared. "Does it make you n-nervous? I should have thought a fellow like you had seen plenty of guns in his time."

"I'd feel happier if you didn't have those two goons waiting outside. They look as though they've been seeing too many James Cagney films. You always go around with them?"

"I'm a careful man, Cayle. As an officer in the Security forces, it would be rather foolish if I n-neglected to look after my own security. But you haven't answered my question. Tell me about yourself."

Cayle took a stiff drink, glanced around the bare walls, then launched into his *curriculum vitae*, very much as he had done a couple of days ago for Hennison, though this time with more leisure and in more detail. Philby listened without interrupting, all the while chain-smoking cheap Russian cigarettes with hollow cardboard stems which he pinched into a filter.

Occasionally he smiled, even laughed, such as when Cayle described his debacle in the Transatlantic Solo race and about when he'd threatened a Red Army colonel in Prague in 1968 by telling the man that "if one hair of my head is touched, every Russian correspondent in London will be hanging in Hyde Park tomorrow morning!"

For the next two hours, while the level of the Osoboya sank inch by inch, Kim Philby and Barry Cayle sat in this bare grubby room high above Moscow and got agreeably drunk together. Apart from the periodic explosions of the plumbing, there were no obstacles; and the only condition that Philby made was that Cayle take no notes, and that no mention be made of Philby's work. From time to time the conversation foundered temporarily on matters of politics, but here Philby was quick to display all the arts of the dialectical gymnast: he was by turns bland, evasive, subtle, and yielding; never dogmatic, never aggressive, but also never defensive, even when Cayle touched on such uncomfortable topics as the Soviet treatment of Jews and dissident intellectuals.

Cayle soon began to like Philby; and with his judgment dimmed by vodka, he found it preposterous to imagine this urbane, boozy, somewhat bedraggled English gent as the Spy of the Century, with a special place in the ranks of Western demonology. Even in this eccentric setting, with the guards outside and the gun in the briefcase, Kim Philby managed to seem such an ordinary fellow. He and Cayle shared many of the same interests, including cricket, cooking, and classical music, as well as having a number of mutual friends who had been Philby's colleagues in the newspaper world. They even had the same birthday—January 1—and drank a toast to the "stubborn and determined" characteristics of Capricorn, while Philby lamented the woes of getting all one's Christmas and birthday presents on the same day—not to mention hangovers.

They finally drained the last of the vodka, and Philby

held up the empty bottle against the feeble light from the window. "I suppose you'll go and write that I'm still up to my bad old habits? Back in the Lebanon I used to have a nickname for this stuff—any stuff, providing it was alcohol. Used to call it 'snakebite.' Only difference was that back there they could mix a decent cocktail. But out here it's rough. One day it's going to kill me. I've got a dicky heart—but I suppose you know that? It's been in the Western press. They're all just hanging on, waiting for me to croak!"

He started to stand up, and paused. "Tell me something, Barry. How do people think of me now in England?"

"Oh, I'd say you have a certain following, Kim—with those who enjoy seeing the nobs get egg all over their faces."

Philby stood for a long time looking at the little window; then he gave Cayle a faint, official nod and said: "It's time you left. The men outside will see you as far as the street. There's a subway station opposite the Pushkin Museum, three blocks from here, if you turn left. You'll find an excellent cigar counter just inside the entrance. You can pick up a Romeo y Julieta corona for thirty kopeks. It's one of the great advantages of living in a Socialist country."

Cayle got to his feet, feeling muddleheaded and sore-eyed from the thick black cigarette smoke. He had started toward the door when Philby added: "Remember, smoking's forbidden on the subway. However, if you feel like enjoying a cigar at the entrance, I might join you."

They shook hands and Cayle crossed to the door.

Cayle's Havana cigar had burned down almost to his

glove, and he was stamping his boots to keep warm, when he saw Philby coming down the steps toward him. He was alone, dressed in the same dark bulky overcoat and black fur hat that he had been wearing yesterday at the Post Office.

He gave Cayle a nod and bought two five-kopek tickets. It was just after midday, and the marble platform, with its vaulted ceiling lined with triple chandeliers, was almost empty. The train slid in a few seconds later, and Philby carefully chose a seat with his back to the platform. Cayle sat opposite, a little to the left of him. Neither of them spoke until they reached the Svedlova station, where Philby got up to leave. Cayle followed at a decent distance.

There was more of a crowd here, most of them in shapeless overcoats and fur hats, and Cayle had to be careful not to lose his escort. At one moment he found himself following a fat middle-aged Muscovite who seemed to be conducting a furious argument with himself. Cayle caught up with Philby just as the latter was boarding the train bound for the Dobryninskaya station, on the Moscow Circle Line.

At Dobryninskaya they followed the same routine. Philby had sauntered to the far end of the platform, where the carriages were less full. Cayle boarded by a different door, and waited until they had passed the first two stops before taking his seat beside Philby, again with their backs to the platform. Philby yawned and stared at the ceiling; he did not seem in the least drunk. "Who sent you here?"

"Officially, my editor. As you probably know, he has a particular interest in your case."

"And unofficially?"

"Fellow called Hennison. Works as a literary agent in London. Said he used to know you during the war when he was on codes."

Philby closed his eyes and nodded. "Donnish sort of fellow. Bit of a snob. Believe he's married to someone called Lady Audrey."

"That's more than I know," said Cayle. "But I can tell you, he doesn't seem to like you much. Said something about you being an A-one copper-bottomed bastard."

"Oh, but I am, old boy! I am. Though Hennison's hardly the one to talk. Still, it was probably just a touch of depression or jealousy." He paused as the train drew in to the Park Kulturi station and a massive woman trundled aboard, laden with soggy brown paper bags. Philby watched as she arranged herself on the seat opposite, then said: "And Hennison gave you the book?"

"He didn't give it to me. He told me the title and I bought it myself."

"You're a good trusting fellow, aren't you, Barry?"

"I'm after a story."

"What sort of story?"

Cayle leaned close to Philby, conscious of the old woman's beady-eyed stare from the seat opposite, and lowered his voice just enough for Philby to hear him above the roar of the wheels. "Tell me, Kim—was there ever a Fourth Man?"

For several seconds Philby sat motionless; then he turned and gave Cayle a slow bleary smile, his eyelids beginning to droop. "You don't think that Guy and Donald and I were the only ones, do you?"

"No, I don't."

"And you're certainly not green enough to think that I'd take a total stranger into my confidence, just on the casual introduction of an old wartime colleague?"

"I don't know what to think," said Cayle. "But there's something you want to tell me."

They passed through Krasnopresnenskaya and Komsomolskaya stations before Philby spoke again. "What the Great Western Public really wants to know is how Colonel Philby of the KGB is making out after thirteen years in Moscow. Well, let me start, Barry, by making a few random observations on the Russian people. They're a fine people, you know. In some ways, the finest in the world. It's just that they're so bloody difficult to live with. Sometimes I really feel almost sorry for them. Wherever they go, they always seem to make themselves so damned unpopular. And I don't mean politically—that's another story. It's the *character* of the race. For instance, you invite a Russian for lunch at one, and he's quite likely to turn up at nine, drunk."

"I should have thought that would have been rather your style, Kim? Bloody sight livelier than British suburbia, with the doorbell going ding-dong on the dot, and everybody standing around with gin-and-tonics, talking about their hotted-up Ford Cortinas."

Philby smiled. "I suppose you're right. God knows, I should be the last to complain. The trouble is, Barry, it seems to work the other way for me. I mean, if I'm invited for lunch, and turn up for dinner pissed, people here take the most ghastly offense. It's not so much that they're hypocrites—it's just that they seem to expect *me* to behave differently. And you know why? Because in their eyes I'm still a bloody English gentleman, and they bloody well demand that I behave like one!"

He paused. They were back at the Dobryninskaya station, and waited while the passengers shunted on and off. As the train moved off again, Philby turned to Cayle and began to speak rapidly, excitedly. It was like the outpouring of a man who has been marooned many months on a desert island.

"What I really can't stand is the way these Russians get drunk—in restaurants, public places—and start fights with the waiters and puke under the tables. I suppose you think I sound squeamish? Well, perhaps I am. But in the capital of the second most powerful country in the world, one wishes people were just a little more *civilized!*"

Cayle laughed. "Kim, I'm beginning to think you're hankering after the old easy life in the West."

Philby looked at him. His expression was grave. "We're all what we were born to be, Barry. I was born a spoiled English upper-middle-class youth with a taste for adventure. Oh, I can do without the luxuries of life—the fast cars and big houses and strings of race horses and beautiful girls. I've never had the least interest in all that. What I miss here is civilized company."

"And the Russians aren't civilized?" said Cayle.

"Oh, don't misunderstand me. I like the Russians. In some ways I think I even love them. I've done enough, God knows, to prove it! The trouble is, they're people you can never really get used to—you're either in tune with them or you're not. It's taken me a long time to realize it, but I just don't fit in with them. It's my loss, not theirs." He stretched his legs and stared mournfully at the ceiling of the carriage. "Hark to the confessions of an old man! Well, I'm certainly not as young as in the old SIS days, though I'm still a long way from the wheelchair. And whenever I get round to thinking about it, I suppose I've got damn little to complain about. Of course, it's not quite the same as when I first got here. They even made me a Hero of the Soviet Union, literally. Actually, it was all a bit of a fraud. My arrival happened to coincide with the craze in the early sixties for mini-skirts and the Beatles and other wicked Western influences. And I, as an upright Britisher of the old school—a gentleman and a Communist to boot—was set up as the antidote. Not that the magic could ever have lasted. Still, I'm treated pretty well. I've got a decent flat. I've got my music and my books—Guy left me his whole library when he died, you know. And I've got a responsible job. Nine-thirty to five-thirty. I'm also bored." His face sagged, and Cayle could see the red linings of his eyes.

"Why are you telling me all this, Kim?"

"You'll want something to write for your paper, won't you? A bit more than a frivolous piece about meeting me over a bottle of vodka and a gun, with two heavies in the corridor outside. If I'm still considered as important in the West as you say I am, I shall presumably be expected to say a few important things."

"Like having a few thoughts about redefecting?"

Philby chuckled. "I deny it. Even if you got your people to print it in the first place."

Cayle looked around and saw they were drawing in to Svedlova station for the second time. He was wondering how long Philby was going to wait before taking the plunge. But as the train pulled out, and Philby still didn't speak, Cayle decided to try head on.

"What made you choose me?"

"Hennison chose you. He's a shifty sod, but he's a shrewd judge of character. I just wonder how long he'd been fishing around before he lighted on you."

"Hennison's not touting a piece about you for my paper, Kim. Or for any other paper. So what the hell's he up to?"

Philby paused. "I shouldn't worry too much about Hennison, if I were you, Barry. It would just complicate things."

"Things seem to be pretty damn complicated already," said Cayle. The air in the train was dry and stale, and he badly needed a long cool drink.

"How's your patience, Barry?" Philby said at last.

"Depends what's at the end of it."

"Something big. Probably the biggest story you ever handled. Exclusive—world rights—the lot."

Cayle sat very still, watching their dim reflections in the windows opposite. Philby went on: "Confidential. Top secret. For your ears only, and nothing in writing. If you break it before I give the okay, I shall deny it, as I said—even if anyone believes it, which is unlikely. I'm a nomad, Barry. Always have been. I pitch my tent, graze my cattle, then move on. I told you just now, I'm bored. I'm ready to strike camp once again. I'm going back into the field, Barry. For one last time."

Cayle turned and blinked at him. "Aren't you taking a bit of a risk telling me this?"

Philby leaned over and patted his knee. "Perhaps you'll understand if I tell you that I've got one last thing to prove—to set the record straight. The last thirteen years haven't been altogether easy ones, you know. Better than a prison cell, perhaps, but not exactly the way of life I'd have chosen if I'd been completely free." He took a deep breath. "You've got to remember that before I came here I'd led a fairly exciting life, by any standards. But I'd had to work undercover—unknown, unrecognized. And when I finally did get to Moscow, certain people said I'd come home." He gave Cayle a baleful stare. "Moscow's not home, Barry. I don't have a home."

"Can I quote you on that?"

Philby shrugged. "I used to be in the business myself, but I always made it a rule never to tell a fellow-journalist how to do his job. In this case it's up to you. You bide your time, and you'll get your story. When I'm ready."

The train was pulling into Dobryninskaya station for the third time, and Philby stood up. "When are you thinking of going back to London?"

"I'll have to get back to write my piece. Even if it's completely harmless, it might not be too tactful sending it out from here."

"No, perhaps not." The doors opened and Philby stepped out onto the mosaic platform. "But remember, stick to telling your Sunday readers how I spend my evenings alone with my cats, listening to Brahms and Schubert. And you might add that I loathe Shostakovich." He strolled past a couple of uniformed militiamen, with Cayle keeping a few feet behind. Only when they were through the barrier did Cayle catch up with him.

"How will I hear from you?"

"You won't. If anything happens, Hennison will call you. And if your editor starts asking tricky questions, just tell him that Kim Philby wants to take you along as his Boswell, to chronicle the final chapter of his eventful but inglorious life."

They had almost reached the top of the steps to the street when Philby turned. "This is where I leave you, Barry. And if you get any ideas about trying to follow me, I'm taking a taxi back to the office. Thirteen Dzerzhinski Square. Anyone'll tell you where it is!"

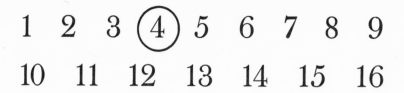

*Laurie, the barman, nodded to him and said,* "Your friend's already here, Mr. Cayle."

At first Cayle almost missed him. He was sitting by himself on a gilt sofa in the corner of the bar, reading the *Financial Times.* They had met only once, in the exclusive Royal Yacht Squadron in Cowes while Cayle had been practicing for the Transatlantic Solo race. All he remembered was a wiry man in oilskins with a pair of frosty eyes under a red woolen pixie hat. But now Sir Roger Jameson-Clarke was restored to the full dignity of a senior Foreign Office official: two wings of immaculate silver hair, elegant beak of nose, chalk-striped suit, quiet regimental tie, and a thin band of wedding ring.

He unfolded his legs from the sofa and offered Cayle a limp cold hand. "I haven't a lot of time," he said, looking at his watch; and Cayle made the usual excuses about the traffic, while Laurie came over for their orders. When they were alone again, Sir Roger went on: "I'd like to make it clear, Mr. Cayle, that this meeting is entirely off the record."

"Well I should hope so, for Christ's sake! You were the one who asked me here. And you surely don't want to chat about spinnakers."

"Please don't be flippant. This is a matter of some importance. And it's not only my department who are interested.

Of course, there is no question of official disapproval for what you wrote. It's merely a question of clarifying certain details, and filling in some of the background."

"You flatter me, sir. Personally, I thought it was a bloody awful piece. It was printed only for the color—and there wasn't much of that."

Sir Roger gave a quick dismissive nod. "Quite. Now, I'd like to take it from the beginning. You picked Philby up at the Post Office?"

"Correct."

"On the off-chance that he'd go along that day and collect his airmail edition of the *Times*?"

"That's right, just as I wrote in Sunday's paper."

Sir Roger waited while Laurie placed their drinks in front of them. "Unfortunately," he said when the barman had left, "I do not entirely believe you."

Cayle smiled. "Is that my cue for saying, 'Are you calling me a liar, sir?' "

"I think you know what I mean. You traveled to Moscow, on no apparent assignment, and on your first day there you happened to run into a certain Englishman who is wanted for high treason by the courts of this country."

"I wasn't breaking any law I know of," said Cayle.

"I'm not suggesting you were. What I want to know is why Philby was willing to talk to you."

"Because he's bored."

"Bored?"

"Yes. He likes to meet people—people from the outside. Westerners. So we had a nice boozy morning together, and he told me how wonderful the Russian people are, but how he can't stand the way they get drunk and fight and are sick all over the place."

"That's rich, coming from him!" Sir Roger muttered. He was never exactly an abstainer himself."

"I suppose you knew him, too?"

"Yes, I knew him. There are very few of my generation who didn't." He licked at his Martini. "He must have had another reason for meeting you."

"I told you—we had a long chat over a bottle of vodka, and he told me he was bored and lonely and wants to go—" Cayle broke off and gulped at his Bacardi-and-orange.

"Yes?" said Sir Roger. "Wants to go where?"

"Oh, shit," said Cayle. "Is this an interview or an interrogation?"

"That rather depends on you. Of course, we have no means—or indeed desire—to pressure you into disclosing information that you'd rather keep secret. But I must point out that there are certain kinds of information that can place their receiver in a rather delicate situation." He sat for a moment studying his perfectly tended fingernails. "Who sent you to see Philby, Mr. Cayle?"

There was a long pause. Cayle signaled to Laurie and started to order two more drinks, but Sir Roger declined. Cayle told Laurie to make his a double. "To hell with it," he said at last. "I was rung up a few weeks ago by a fellow called Hennison—literary agent who wants me to write a novel about Philby. He suggested I take him a Graham Greene novel as a present—just to smooth the way, so to speak."

Sir Roger Jameson-Clarke sat very still. "Which novel was that?" he asked gently.

"One of his early ones—*The Confidential Agent.*"

"And was that your choice?"

"No, Hennison suggested it. He said it was one of Philby's favorites."

Sir Roger Jameson-Clarke's cold marine eyes were fixed on the chandelier above Cayle's head. "You started to say that Philby wanted to go somewhere. Where, Mr. Cayle?"

"He used the expression 'go out into the field again.' "

Sir Roger still stared at the chandelier, and his voice was weary. "And what do you suppose he meant by that?"

"I'd have thought that would have been more in your department," said Cayle. "Isn't 'the field' more or less the same as 'the cold'?"

"Yes, yes, I know. But what do you think he really meant? He's far too old for the Russians to start using him again as an active agent."

"Well, I guess old Kim's much like the rest of us—can't bear the idea of settling down and growing roses for the rest of his life. He wants to have one last fling—to set the record straight, as he put it."

"Were those the words he used—'set the record straight'?"

"More or less."

There was a pause. Sir Roger seemed to be thinking of something else: his eyes were remote, his patrician cheeks pale. "Set the record straight," he repeated. "And I suppose you've no idea what he meant by that, either?"

"No," said Cayle truthfully. "No idea at all."

Cayle had washed up the remains of his Chinese dinner, put on Brahms' Symphony No. 4, and had just begun playing solo Scrabble when the phone rang. It was the editor.

"Barry—just had a call from Ron. Your FO friend you saw today at the Ritz has gone AWOL."

"What?"

"Sir Roger Jameson-Clarke. They found his car abandoned two hours ago near his home at a little place called Stonor, outside Henley. Seems there's quite a flap on. Thames Valley Police have apparently called in the Special Branch."

"Did Ron get all this?"

"That's right—contact of his at the Yard. Hasn't been put out yet. If you hurry you could be first there. But play it close. I wouldn't let on about you and Sir Roger—not yet, anyway."

"You think there's some connection?"

"Do you?"

Cayle paused. He could feel the pulse in his thumb twitching against the receiver. "I don't see how—"

"Get moving," said the editor. "And ring me at home when you're through. I don't mind how late it is."

They hung up simultaneously. Cayle grabbed his Pentax and flash, checked that he had all his press cards, then sprang down the stairs four steps at a time.

It was just 12:10. The traffic on the Hammersmith overpass was light, and the night dry and clear. He was on the M4 ten minutes after leaving the flat, and with his foot down and the wind shrieking under the canvas flaps of the Mini-Moke, he reached the intersection off to Henley and Oxford by 12:50.

He used a brief pause at the traffic lights in Henley to check the map for Stonor, which was five miles beyond the town on the Watlington Road. He drove through the darkened village at sixty, and found the spot without trouble, a quarter of a mile farther on. Two Panda cars and a white Jaguar with a fluorescent orange stripe down the side were parked on the verge next to an open five-bar gate. A motorcycle patrolman was leaning in through the window of the Jaguar, and the radio on his machine was jabbering like a nest of wasps. He turned too late; Cayle had already turned off the road and swung past him, and the Moke was now bouncing down a muddy track between open fields.

The rest of them were around a bend under some trees leading down to the river. There were three cars here: a police Rover with a flashing blue light, a second Jaguar, with no insignia, and a dark handsome Alvis drawn up a light farther along under the trees. There were about half a dozen uniformed men with powerful flashlights, and a couple of dogs nosing about in the muddy bank beyond the Alvis.

Cayle pulled up at a discreet distance and got out without haste, keeping his camera under his anorak, and began to stroll toward the cars. A radio was putting out a call signal from the Rover and a constable with bushy sideburns was talking to an inspector beside the Jaguar. There was also a thickset man in a short brown sheepskin coat, watching the dogs.

Cayle was just crossing the track opposite the first car when he was challenged. "Excuse me, sir." It was the Inspector.

Cayle showed him his Scotland Yard press pass, but the man was not visibly impressed. "Who gave you permission to come through?"

"Nobody stopped me," said Cayle. The constable had edged forward and was staring at him with a suspicious countryman's face.

"This is a restricted area," said the Inspector.

"There was nothing to say so," Cayle replied, just as the man in the sheepskin coat walked up to them and without a word took Cayle's press pass from the Inspector's hand. He stood reading it carefully, compared Cayle with the photograph, turned it over, and said, "Barry Cayle? Don't I know you from somewhere? You were on the box a few weeks ago, sailing round the world?"

"Almost." Cayle nodded at the Alvis under the trees. "What's going on?"

"You mean you don't know?" the man said, in a flat toneless voice.

Cayle shrugged. "Something about an aban
I was told."

"Who told you?"

"I work for a big organization. Better ask th
got a phone call telling me to come out here."

The man stood watching him with muddy eyes. "What's
the particular interest?"

"About the same as yours, I should say. It's a nice car.
The owner must be proud of it. They don't make them any
more. Seems funny to dump it out in a place like this in
the middle of the night."

"Any theories?"

"Maybe he's a nature fetishist and went for a midnight
swim. Or perhaps he's crept off to smoke pot?"

"Don't be cheeky, Cayle." One of the flashlights swung
around and the man's complexion showed up hard and
lumpy, like cold porridge. "I asked you a question. What
brought you here?"

"I told you. A phone call."

The man sighed and squared his shoulders. "You know
who the car belongs to?"

"Should I?"

"Don't arse around—this is important."

"Yeah, I rather got that impression. You know, you'll
have half Fleet Street swarming all over this place by
morning. But we don't publish till Saturday night."

"Meaning what?"

Cayle shrugged. "Gives you plenty of time to start slap-
ping on the 'D' notices."

"They've been abolished. Don't you know that?"

"Just a figure of speech," said Cayle, "seeing there might
be a Security angle."

"Nobody said anything about a Security angle. It's just

. routine check—may turn out to be nothing. One of the gardeners had left some tobacco down here and came back to get it, and found the car about ten-fifty. He reported it to Lady Jameson-Clarke, who notified the police. She'd been expecting her husband back for dinner."

"And nobody saw the car drive in here?"

"We haven't found anybody yet. It's all private property round here."

"His property?"

The man nodded, and began to turn.

"What about the hospitals?" said Cayle.

"We've got a call out. Nothing yet."

"And London airport?"

"What about London airport?"

"It's less than half an hour away, if you drive fast."

The man looked at him steadily and said, "All right, that's the lot. Run along."

Cayle opened his anorak and aimed the Pentax at the Alvis and the dogs under the trees. For a moment he thought the man was going to jump him, but he stepped smartly out of the frame just as the flash went off. Cayle was able to get only the one shot before the camera was pushed back against his chest.

"I could have you for this, you bastard," the man said quietly; and Cayle felt a hand close around his arm. It was the Inspector's. "I told you—this is a restricted area," he said.

Cayle grinned at the man in the sheepskin coat. "What's the matter, sport? Shy of having your picture taken?"

"If you're not away from here in one minute, Cayle, I'll have you for trespass and obstruction—just for a start. Now bugger off."

"Go on," said the Inspector. "You heard."

One of them trod on his heels as they followed him back

to the Mini-Moke. Cayle slipped into reverse and lurched back from them. They watched him as far as the bend, where he was just able to turn around. The men at the entrance to the track gave him no trouble, and he was back at his flat in Thackeray Mansions, off the North End Road, by 2:30. He fixed himself a stiff Scotch and rang the editor, who answered at once: "Well?"

"Just as you said. AWOL since before dinner. And his car's parked down a farm track on his own land. According to the map, it's about half a mile from the river. They've already got dogs on the job, as well as an SB man, who seemed rather less friendly than usual. I took a pic, which he didn't like at all. So you may hear from someone."

"Don't worry, we look after our own." The editor sounded cheerful, even at 2:30 in the morning. "How does it strike you?" he added.

"A bit odd. I mean, they've moved in on it bloody fast. Normally, you'd expect the local fuzz to keep it to themselves for at least twenty-four hours."

"And you think it's something big?"

"If he doesn't turn up pretty quick, I'd say it was bloody big!"

There was a pause. "Listen, Barry, I think we'd better continue to play this very carefully. I don't want a word about tonight, or about yesterday at the Ritz—not even to Ron or Bruce—until I say."

"What happens if the fuzz start asking questions?"

"I think we deal with that when it happens. We still don't know that a crime's been committed, remember."

"What do you think, Harry? Do the Russkies still go in for rough stuff?"

"Highly unlikely. Last case was in Germany back in the early sixties, I think. But that was a refugee they knocked off with a cyanide bullet. Hardly the sort of thing you'd expect in a quiet country lane in Oxfordshire."

"No," said Cayle. "Any more than you'd expect a traitor to be a member of the Athenaeum."

The editor chuckled. "Good night, Barry, and get a good sleep. You may need it."

Sir Roger Jameson-Clarke made the BBC's "World at One" and the front-page leads in both London evening papers: MYSTERY OF MISSING DIPLOMAT and YARD HUNT TOP DIPLOMAT. But from the stories themselves it was clear that the news editors were having the same problems as the police, and were grabbing at anything that looked like an angle, however remote. Scotland Yard had put out a statement that they were "not ruling out foul play"; and the early TV bulletins carried interviews with Lady Jameson-Clarke, a handsome woman with frothy hair who seemed almost as concerned about how last night's dinner had been ruined as about the loss of her husband.

Cayle had been back at Thackeray Mansions for an hour, and was going through Sir Roger Jameson-Clarke's envelope of press clippings from his paper's library when they called.

The bell was broken, and they had to give a couple of loud knocks. "Evening, Cayle. Mind if we have a word with you?" He was still in his sheepskin coat and had his foot inside the door as soon as Cayle opened it. He held up a card in a celluloid holder. "Special Branch, Sergeant Dempster. This is Mr. Mayhew."

Behind him stood a balding man in a mackintosh who might have been from the Ministry of Pensions. Dempster stood aside to let him through. Mayhew nodded. "I hope this isn't inconvenient, sir?"

"Any time." Cayle waved them both into the sitting room. "Drink?"

They shook their heads and remained standing, without removing their coats. Cayle turned to the dresser and poured himself a canned beer.

"You live here alone?" Dempster said; he was looking down at the unfinished Scrabble game on the table.

"On and off," said Cayle. "It's not an offense, is it?"

"It's an offense to withhold information from the police, Mr. Cayle."

"Like what?"

"Like not telling us last night that you knew Sir Roger Jameson-Clarke."

"I wasn't asked."

"Sure, sure." Dempster gave a tight humorless smile. "I'd better tell you that we checked his appointment book. He had a date yesterday for twelve at the Ritz. No name, but the barman downstairs confirmed that he'd been there. Seems he's a friend of yours—the barman, I mean. Told us you talked with Jameson-Clarke for about half an hour. Right?"

"Right," said Cayle.

"Why didn't you tell us that this morning?" said Dempster.

"I might have, if you hadn't been so unpleasant."

"Sensitive, are you?"

"You'd be surprised!"

They faced each other in morose silence. Mayhew, who had been quietly filling a knobbly black pipe from a plastic pouch, said: "Would you mind telling us what you and Sir Roger talked about?"

Cayle took a deep drink and said carefully: "I came back from Moscow last week. Sir Roger wanted me to fill him in on a few things. It was a routine chat. A lot of the FO boys do it. Keeping in touch."

Mayhew put a match to his pipe and sucked at it with a slow wheeze. "How did Sir Roger seem to you yesterday, Mr. Cayle?"

"How do you mean?"

"Did he appear anxious? Nervous? Worried about something?"

"Well, he wasn't trembling in fear of his life, if that's what you mean."

Mayhew looked at him for a moment with quiet, deep-set eyes. "We know from his secretary that he canceled an appointment yesterday, to meet you."

"Really? I should be flattered."

"I think you should be concerned," said Mayhew. "It may well be that you were one of the last people to see him."

"The last? You mean, he's kicked the bucket?"

"I didn't say that. Now, just try to remember exactly what you both discussed. It's just that Sir Roger may have said something—something apparently quite innocuous—which might give us an idea of where he's gone. Try to remember, Mr. Cayle."

Cayle fetched himself another can of beer and told them about how he'd met Sir Roger down at the Squadron in Cowes last summer, when they'd both been messing about in boats. As for the Moscow trip, Sir Roger had been interested in the usual background impressions—the general atmosphere of the city, what the locals were talking about, what sort of people they were, and how they reacted to a foreign journalist.

While he was talking, Sergeant Dempster walked across the room and began examining the bookshelves. Cayle watched him take out several copies and leaf through them; they were from a corner he kept for works on international espionage. Dempster pushed one of them back into the shelf and turned. "Very interested in Kim Philby, aren't you?"

"Aren't we all?"

"I wouldn't say all. Some of us, maybe. But you seem to be a real fan—you got half a dozen books on the bastard."

"I'm thinking of writing a book on him myself. You might even get a warrant to read the first draft."

Dempster gave him a blank stare. Mayhew was peering into the bowl of his pipe. He said, without looking up: "You met Philby in Moscow last week, I understand, Mr. Cayle?"

"That's what the story said."

"Yes, quite. And I expect, no doubt, the subject of this meeting came up in your talk yesterday with Sir Roger Jameson-Clarke?"

"I think it was mentioned."

Mayhew knocked out his pipe into an ashtray. "Well, thank you, Mr. Cayle. I'm sorry we had to trouble you. By the way, will you be going abroad in the next few days?"

"Better check with my editor."

"Yes, we will. Good night, Mr. Cayle."

Cayle opened the door for him, then paused. "You didn't ever run into Kim Philby yourself, did you, Mr. Mayhew?"

Mayhew suddenly smiled: it was as though an electric light had been switched on inside his skull and lit up his sunken eyes like a halloween mask. "Yes, as a matter of fact I did. Never got on with him, though. About the only thing we had in common was the same birthday."

Cayle laughed. "Don't tell me—another poor kid who got all his presents on Christmas Day?"

"I'm afraid I don't follow you."

"You were born on New Year's Day—a Capricorn." He grinned. "Stubborn and determined."

"No, Mr. Cayle, my birthday's in October."

The editor lifted the red house phone, pushed down a switch, and said, "Alistair? Godfrey here. How are your contacts with the secret boys?" He listened, then nodded. "Man called Mayhew—could be CID or Special Branch, but more likely MI5." There was a pause. "Yes? Yes, right. That's marvelous, Alistair. Many thanks."

He hung up and turned to Cayle. "You were right. Your friend Mayhew's one of Five's liaison men with the Home Office. Mostly deals with counterespionage against the Soviet bloc. You're getting the full treatment, Barry."

"Hell I am. What do I do now—wait for them to come for me with the meat wagon?"

"I don't think you need worry. You haven't done anything wrong, yet." He paused. "I'll tell you what I'm going to do, Barry. I'm going to give you a straight choice. You can either take a three-week holiday—anywhere within reason, providing it's abroad. Or you can follow up that tip you got in Moscow about a Franco-Soviet aircraft deal." He held up his hand. "I know—it's not your line of country, but it won't do you any harm to diversify."

Cayle thought: You crafty old sod! Mustn't be seen subsidizing amateur secret missions to Moscow, or catering to the vanity of an archtraitor; but you can't pass up the chance of a good story, either.

The editor was keeping his options open. He said, "By the way, how would a Soviet citizen go about escaping to the West?"

"Well, I'd say that if he happened to be a KGB colonel, he could probably swing something with the Frontier

Police, who are a branch of the KGB. He'd probably use a fairly remote border post—somewhere down in the Soviet Asiatic republics, and get over into Turkey or Iran."

The editor drummed his fingers on the desk top. "And how would a Westerner get into the Soviet Union without a visa?"

"You mean legally?"

The editor nodded.

"Well, there's Leningrad," Cayle said. "You sign on for a day trip over from Helsinki by sea, which you can do without a visa, and you manage to miss the boat back in the evening. The trouble with that method is you have to surface pretty quickly, or risk being run in. In other words, the most you get is a few hours on the loose before the next boat sails."

"What's the most you could get—another way?"

"Seventy-two hours. But it's expensive. You go to Afghanistan, check in on an Aeroflot flight from Kabul to Russia—Tashkent, and on to Moscow. Once you're with Aeroflot's internal services, you get an automatic forty-eight-hour transit visa, with a further twenty-four-hour extension if you miss your connecting flight to the West. In theory, you could go on getting extensions indefinitely, providing you could come up each time with a good enough excuse."

"How do you manage to shake off the Intourist people?"

"Ah, well, that's the beauty of it! On the internal routes they don't check you into an Intourist hotel at all. In Moscow you get dumped in the Aeroflot Hotel, a couple of miles out of town, with three thousand guests from all over the USSR arriving in busloads day and night. And apart from the floor bouncers, there are no official guides—nobody to know you're even a Westerner, if you dress right. You just get in the elevator and ride down to the subway station, which is bang under the hotel, and take a train to anywhere in the city."

"And all perfectly legal?"

"Perfectly. Providing your ticket's in order."

The editor was staring out the window. "How would you like to take a holiday in Afghanistan, Barry?"

Cayle gave a slow, sour grin. "With all expenses paid?"

"If you agree."

"What happened, Godfrey?"

"The Russian Embassy was on to us this morning—a sort of pre-emptive call. They informed us, very politely, that there is no need for you to apply for another visa. You won't get it."

"I see. Is that all they said?"

"They did mention that if you applied again in a few months, they might get another reply from Moscow. The Foreign Desk asked them if they would contact us when they heard from Moscow, but they said, 'When we hear from Moscow, you contact us.' "

"Very funny. And no reasons?"

"None. I suppose we can safely assume that any Westerner who's been nosing around Philby is bad news."

"There was nothing in my piece that could possibly have offended either Philby or the KGB."

"No," said the editor. "Unless it was someone else, using their influence."

Cayle said nothing. The editor went on: "I'm not in any way trying to pressure you, Barry. You must make up your own mind. But if you do decide to go, may I make a suggestion? Start your trip from somewhere other than London. Fly to Paris or Amsterdam, and then get your ticket to Kabul. And pay for it in cash."

"You've got it all worked out, haven't you, Godfrey?"

"Well, I did take the precaution of applying for an Afghan transit visa for you. It should be through tomorrow morning."

Cayle again checked the cars parked outside Thackeray Mansions; they were all empty, including his Mini-Moke.

It was still dark, but the juggernaut traffic was already building up along Finborough Road, where he caught a taxi to Heathrow and told the driver to drop him at the British Airways entrance of Number Two Building. There he checked in for the 8:00 A.M. flight to Paris, and bought all the morning papers.

Sir Roger was still holding his own on most of the front pages; there were photographs of him with the Queen, the PM, with sundry Heads of State, and most recently in a box at Covent Garden. The stories themselves, though still lame for lack of information, were full of sinister promise. Sir Roger had not been found. The Thames was being dragged for another five miles on either side of Stonor, and dog patrols and civilian volunteers were searching all woods and waste ground as far as Watlington and Marlow. Several papers made the point that Sir Roger had been happily married to his third wife, which seemed to rule out suicide; and there was a report—which the Home Office refused to confirm or deny—that a special watch was being kept on all sea and air ports, and that the police forces of Western Europe had been alerted.

At seven o'clock the first call went out for Flight BA 307 to Zürich. Cayle folded the newspapers under his arm and made his way down to the departure gate. "You're on the Paris flight, sir," the girl said as he handed her his boarding card. "It's not due to be called till a quarter to eight."

"I know," he said; "I like to give myself lots of time in the duty-free shop." He walked through and showed his passport to Immigration.

"Where are you going, sir?"

"Zürich."

The man nodded and handed his passport back. A second official glanced at him, then stared past his shoulder at the passengers behind. Cayle walked through to the departure lounge.

Two hours later he was at Orly. The CRS at French Passport Control had shown no interest in him; they had been told to look out for a distinguished British diplomat with a pedigree that went back to the Norman Conquest.

Cayle checked out his luggage, drank half a bottle of champagne at the bar, changed $500 of American Express traveler's checks into cash, then bought a single ticket to Athens on Olympic Airlines. When the flight was called, only one passenger caught his eye—a florid little man with swept-back grey hair who followed him through the departure gate, showing a British passport. On the plane he sat in the row behind Cayle, but at Athens he disappeared.

Cayle now booked a seat with Air France on a flight leaving Athens that afternoon for Teheran. As he came aboard, the stewardesses were handing out copies of a French evening paper, which carried photographs not only of Sir Roger, but also of Guy Burgess, Donald Maclean, and Kim Philby. With Gallic glee, and untroubled by threats of libel, the black headlines proclaimed: NOUVEL SCANDALE D'ESPION EN ANGLETERRE? DIPLOMAT DISPARU SÈME LA PANIQUE À LONDRES!

He had been served a tray of pâté, *bœuf en croûte*, Boursin, and half a bottle of Volnay, when he spotted the little man with the swept-back hair, sitting a few rows ahead of him this time. The sight gave Cayle a pleasurable thrill, and he ordered a large brandy with his coffee, switched on the reading light, and settled back to enjoy the last tortured days of Scobie, in his steamy outpost in wartime West Africa. It was a Penguin edition this time. Hennison had not specified an edition, only the title: *The Heart of the Matter*.

They touched down at Teheran shortly after midnight, local time. It was a chill starless night, and the terminal was empty except for a few lethargic officials and a man in pantaloons pushing a mop across the floor, pausing every few minutes to spit into a pail of sand.

While they waited for the luggage to come through, Cayle strolled over to a locked souvenir shop and glanced at the goods in the darkened window. A man stood close to him and nodded. "Handsome bugger, isn't he?" His swept-back hair had fallen over his ears and he looked hot and sweaty. He nodded again at a black plastic bust of the Shah on a chromium pedestal. "Reza the Second. One of the sods that screws us for oil."

"You always drink on duty?" said Cayle.

The man blinked at him, then laughed. "Think I've had one or two, do you? As a matter of fact I've had eight. It's flying that does it, see. Always think the wings are going to drop off. One day they will, too—I know it."

"That why you changed planes in Athens?"

"Ah, you're a smart one, you are!" He gave him a slap on the arm, and Cayle dropped *The Heart of the Matter*. "Whoops!" the man cried, and picked it up off the floor. "Going far?" he added.

"Stick around and find out."

The man chuckled, and glanced around the hall. The

luggage was coming through. "Bar's closed," he said. "All the children go to bed. Talk about the exotic East—you could have more fun in Tooting bloody Bec!"

"I'll see you on the plane," said Cayle.

"You going on to Delhi?"

"Who knows?" Cayle began to walk away, and the man called: "Hey, don't you want your book?"

"Thanks," said Cayle. He went over and collected his luggage, then checked at the desk, where he was told the next flight to Kabul didn't leave until eight in the morning. But there was a hotel at the airport where he was assigned a single-bedded concrete cell with a cupboard-sized bathroom on the eighth floor.

It was still only 1:30 A.M., four hours ahead of London time, and he couldn't sleep. He took a shower and dressed and went downstairs. The bar and restaurant were closed. A couple of black-eyed men in heavy lamb's-wool coats were handing in their keys, then walked out through the entrance and got into a chauffeur-driven Mercedes.

Cayle went out after them and started walking down a deserted avenue under high strips of bluish light. The only sounds were the occasional boom of aircraft and choruses of wild dogs shrieking out of the darkness on either side. Ahead lay the orange blur of the city. He had been walking for about ten minutes, and was thinking about the little Englishman with the red face and swept-back hair.

He never knew what saved him. He heard nothing above the noise of the dogs, and the car was driving with side lights only. Perhaps it was a last split-second reaction to the shock waves of air, making him leap sideways and stumble on the broken curb as the car swept past with a roaring slipstream that made his trousers flap. He had time to see only that it was a dark-colored Citroën; but he never saw the driver or the number plate.

He picked himself up and shivered; he had left his anorak at the hotel. Then he realized that he'd been on the wrong side of the road. At the same moment all the dogs went quiet, and he was aware of a breathless hush. He started back to the hotel fast.

In the elevator he caught his reflection in the mirror: there were white rings around his eyes and he was sweating. Steady, he thought. He wanted to hear Harry's gentle monotone telling him to take a holiday in the sun; he didn't care any more about Philby and his secret shifty world of plain-clothes cops and gentlemen robbers, or even what had become of that old mandarin Sir Roger Jamesson-Clarke. He was suddenly very tired; but as soon as he was in bed again, he rang down and asked for an alarm call for 5:30.

There was no sign of the Englishman next morning, either at breakfast in the hotel or when Cayle boarded the Ariana Viscount for the three-hour flight to Kabul.

They landed at the Afghan capital at noon, with a high wind shrieking off the mountain, carrying swirls of dust off the tarmac that cut Cayle's eyes, even under the fastened hood of his anorak. He stumbled half-blinded into the terminal, where a row of khaki-faced men with ferocious mustaches and knitted ear muffs sat chewing fudge as they stamped passports, chalked luggage, and nodded people into the Arrivals hall.

The Aeroflot office was behind a locked door with a chipped inscription in Russian, Afghan, and English, announcing that it would reopen at three o'clock. There was no left-luggage office, no restaurant, no bar. Cayle carried his case outside, and after trudging for some time down broad dusty tracks, found a windowless café lined with silent men in skullcaps, smoking elaborately curved pipes.

They reminded him of a row of painted chocolate dolls. One of them stared at him as he entered, then ducked through a bead curtain and reappeared with a plate of charred kebab. There seemed no question of Cayle refusing it or ordering anything else. He took it over to an empty chair and ate it off his upended suitcase. There were no tables. No one spoke to him or took the least notice of him.

Two hours later he returned to the Aeroflot office and bought his single ticket to London, via Tashkent and Moscow. He received his forty-eight-hour visa without demur for an extra payment of five U.S. dollars, including airport tax. Outside, the wind had not slackened. The plane was a heavy-bellied twin-prop Tupolov which Cayle guessed was a converted bomber; the seams of its skin were stained with ancient rust, and the interior was stark and functional, like a ramshackle bus.

One of the engines choked and belched smoke past the windows; oil slicks spat across the wings; the floor shuddered, swayed, and finally lifted. Barry Cayle sat back and waited for the wine and *kvas*.

# 1 2 3 4 ⑤ 6 7 8 9
# 10 11 12 13 14 15 16

*Monsieur Charles Pol spent a wretchedly event-*
ful five days after arriving in Moscow.

They began with a small calamity at Copenhagen's
Kastrup Airport, where his plane stopped en route from
Paris. The passengers were deposited at the farther gate
from the transit lounge, linked by almost a kilometer of
corridor, which the Danes had thoughtfully equipped
with push-scooters. Handled with care, these could reach
speeds of up to fifteen miles an hour; and Pol, whose im-
mense weight did not encourage walking, gratefully
availed himself of one. He did well for the first few hundred yards, until he tried to negotiate a right-angled bend
and collided with a couple of imposing blondes. Being a
chivalrous man, he made a desperate attempt to avoid
them, jerking the front wheel to the left and jamming his
tiny foot to the floor, and had bounced off both of them
and finished up in a tumbled mass against the wall. When
the two girls had managed to lift him to his feet he found
he couldn't walk.

He was treated at the first-aid center, where they bound
up his ankle so thickly that he was unable to squeeze on his
small fur-lined boot, and had to be transported back to
the plane in a wheelchair. For the rest of the journey the
pain had been softened by copious champagne in the
first-class compartment, so that by the time they began
their descent over the dark wastes toward Moscow, Pol was
feeling euphoric.

( 97

This state of mind ended abruptly at Sheremetyevo Airport. Here there was not only no wheelchair to meet him, but also no official limousine. By some oversight the usual VIP treatment accorded to the president of an international company engaged in a multimillion-ruble deal with the Soviet government had been scheduled for the wrong day. Instead, Pol was subjected to the tedious rigors of Soviet Customs and Immigration, during which his three oyster-white Louis Vuitton suitcases were searched and a French magazine confiscated.

But Charles Pol was a patient man, and despite his injured foot, he accepted a taxi into the city. A few hundred yards from the Hotel Intourist, at an intersection on Gorki Street, his driver slammed on the brakes and the taxi slid smoothly into the side of a bus. A lengthy argument followed, involving both drivers, several militiamen and a crowd of bystanders; and Pol was at last allowed to leave his luggage and hobble the remaining few hundred yards through freezing snow, to reach the hotel with the elephantine bandage on his foot reduced to a sopping sponge that left wet marks across the deep-pile carpet.

Fortunately, in this most modern of Russian hotels, where piped music plays in all the elevators and toilets, Pol was a familiar and honored guest. His suite was equipped with three telephones, push-button radio, color television, soap and towels, and a bowl of crystallized fruit "with the fraternal compliments of Intourist." Two hours after his arrival his suitcases were brought up, scarred and spattered with mud.

His next day began with exhausting efficiency. He was awakened at 8:30 A.M. by a phone call from the Ministry of

Trade. A car arrived for him half an hour later, and he was driven to a series of lavatory-tile palaces; passed from one scrupulously polite official to another, each accompanied by a pedantic interpreter; served refreshments consisting of biscuits and sweet black tea, while piles of documents were produced and translated and discussed, but never signed.

In the evening he learned that he was booked to see *Swan Lake* at the Bolshoi. Pol disliked the ballet, and Tchaikovsky in particular; but with a subtlety rare among Russians, his hosts implied that a refusal would not be acceptable. His foot was still swollen and painful; and the performance, with three fifteen-minute intervals, lasted four hours. Afterward, he was entertained at a banquet where toasts were drunk to Franco-Soviet friendship and to certain French political figures whose names were almost as distasteful to him as the sweet Georgian wines.

His spirits sagged, his foot throbbed, and he longed for his vine-trellised patio above Lac Leman, with his Corsican manservant pouring him Dom Perignon from a chilled bottle wrapped in a white napkin. His deal with Aeroflot, he reflected, should bring him a profit of nearly five million French francs. He was beginning to wonder if it was worth it.

Next day his doubts became misgivings. The enigmatic machinery of Soviet State bureaucracy slipped into top gear. This time it was a Volga sedan that collected him from the hotel and drove at high speed, with its headlights on full beam and the militiamen at the intersections holding up the traffic with their lighted batons. They drew up in front of a building that looked like a prewar radio set, where he was escorted by plain-clothes officials into a room lined with marble cherubs and grave, pale men in black suits sitting on either side of a long table. Pol was shown to a seat near the top, next to a man who was introduced as the Deputy Minister of Transport.

The first two hours passed with the usual preambles through interpreters, and the exchange of documents. Then the trouble started. Until now Pol had been dealing with the financial experts, whose job was to haggle over prices; but gradually, ominously, it became apparent to him that several of the dark-suited men at this meeting were not the usual state functionaries, but scientists and aeronautical engineers. The laborious mouthings of negotiation began to give way to questions—many of which, to Pol's growing dismay, were addressed directly to him, often in fluent French.

But he refused to lose his nerve. Russian bureaucrats, he told himself, were like animals: they only grew *méchants* when they smelled fear. And Pol had nothing to fear; he had not been openly dishonest in his dealings. All the invoices and bills of conveyance were in order, up to a point. They specified that the engines of the aircraft, which he was negotiating to sell to Aeroflot, in order to help restock their fleet of aging Tupolovs, were modern. It was just that the bodies into which they were fitted, while renovated, were in many cases more than a decade old; and the Russian experts had discovered that at least three of them were Nord Atlas transport planes that had probably seen service in Algeria.

The mood of the Russians turned chilly. However, Pol was a man of spirit who enjoyed a challenge. He argued, blustered, prevaricated, lied, even wept; he puffed and swelled with outraged pride, claiming that if anything was wrong it was the fault of Capitalist cartels and unnamed banking interests who had swindled all of them together.

His protestations were only partly successful. Most of the experts showed their contempt by leaving; but the bureaucrats stayed to haggle over more documents, more figures and dates and details. The Deputy Minister also remained; for Pol still held his trump card: the giant Troika-Caravelle airbus, whose maiden flight for the benefit of the international press was now scheduled to take off from Leningrad next week. Pol's company was the sole agent for the enterprise, and he lost little time in making clear to the Deputy Minister that should either his own or his company's reputations be impugned, he might be inclined to solicit other clients. The Argentinian government had shown interest, he said.

The Deputy Minister was politely enigmatic; and Pol knew that he was on probation. He was peeved rather than worried. The situation represented not so much a financial threat as an affront to his judgment; for until now he had entertained many warm illusions about the Soviet Union. These included a firm opinion that where business matters were concerned, the Russians were a soft touch. Any modern nation, he argued, which ordered its affairs according to the teachings of an exiled German Jew who had died in London more than a century ago could be no match for the fiscal agility of Charles Pol.

At the same time he was aware that in any country with a sensible and alert administration he might now be in serious trouble. But here in Russia—while he went on blindly swearing that any irregularities were the work of malign forces in the West—the Soviet officials also began passing blame and responsibility on to anonymous superiors, each reluctant to risk being the cause of an embarrassing diplomatic row with a friendly Western power.

Pol was also helped by his appearance. Vast, pink, and pear-shaped, with a goatee beard and kiss curl pasted across his brow, he looked at first like a comic professor out of a nineteenth-century farce. But there was something about the very enormity of him, and the occasional gleam in those impish eyes, that suggested a man of substance, if not integrity. Even his little cherry lips and his shrill, almost girlish laugh might be thought, correctly, to be deceptive.

Charles Pol was an opportunist, a sybarite, and a hypocrite. He was also a ruthless idealist who saw nothing improper about championing the cause of the underdog, while lining his pocket with a handsome percentage for his pains. The making of money was an amusing game for Pol, a means of scoring off his sillier brethren, as well as supplying him with the necessary luxuries of life. His real passion—besides food and drink—was to play *deus ex machina;* and the possible collapse of his deal with Aeroflot now seemed to open up a nice opportunity for this.

It had been some weeks since his meeting with the Englishman on his last visit to Moscow. While renegade English gentlemen were not a breed that Pol particularly admired, in this case the sheer scope and audacity of the man's career made Pol naturally sympathetic. He even felt a roguish affinity with Monsieur Philby.

After only a few hours together, Pol knew there were great possibilities, providing he moved with care. The man was an alcoholic, a disillusioned expatriate, half idealist, half troublemaker. He also had charm and intelligence; but, more important, he was possibly an even higher priest of perfidy than Pol himself. And like a grand chess master who has grown weary of easy victories, so Pol had quickened to the promise of a really worthy opponent.

He was soon anticipating a dramatic scheme into which the Englishman would fit admirably. If it succeeded, not only would it gratify Pol's perverse sense of ethics, but also he saw a way of turning it to some financial advantage. London, he knew, was even tighter on the purse strings than Paris, but he calculated that once he applied the right pressures, reason would prevail. The British, he told himself, were a very reasonable race.

His only concern now was that the Aeroflot deal would collapse completely, and that he might even be ordered to leave the country. However, while his relations with the Soviet authorities did not improve, they were not discontinued; his visa was not withdrawn and he continued to occupy the suite in the Hotel Intourist, which he also used as an office.

In the evening, following his nearly disastrous conference with the Deputy Minister, Pol put into motion the first stage of his master plan. He called at the British Embassy in Naberezhnaya Morisa Toreza.

Cayle began his first full day in Moscow by going into his bathroom on the twelfth floor of the Hotel Aeroflot and biting off a lump of soap. He swallowed it, washed out his mouth with malt whisky, cleaned his teeth to get rid of the smell, then went along to the elevators. He had neglected to shave.

He did not feel well as he rode down, surrounded by fur-coated Asiatics smelling of cheap scent, and got out at the third floor, where a slim aluminum replica of the TU-144, the Soviet rival to Concorde, stood on a plinth in front of the Aeroflot booking desk. Several people eyed him warily as he joined the queue with head bowed, his air ticket to London gripped in a clammy fist. When he finally reached the woman at the desk, he looked pleadingly down at her and said, "You speak English?"

"I do."

"I'm booked to go to London this morning."

She glanced inside his ticket and nodded. "The bus will leave the hotel in ten minutes. You must hurry."

Cayle blinked at her and his mouth hung open. "Excuse me," he growled, "but I am ill."

"You are staying in the hotel?"

"I'm in transit. From Afghanistan. I arrived last night, and I think I'm sick." He leaned against the desk and gripped his belly.

"One moment, please." She whispered to one of her companions, then turned to him and said, "I will keep this ticket and will make other arrangements. Now you will go to your room and wait."

Cayle obeyed. Twenty minutes later a key turned in the lock and three women marched in. Two of them wore white coats, and one carried a black bag. The third was the woman from the Aeroflot desk. They stood in a row beside the bed, while the one with the bag began fitting a gauze mask across her nose and mouth.

Cayle started to sit up, but the Aeroflot woman pushed him down again, then spoke rapidly in Russian. The one with the mask nodded, leaned over the bed and pressed a hard finger into the center of his stomach. He yelled, and she grunted something through the mask. The Aeroflot woman said: "You must tell where the pain is."

"The pain's all over," Cayle moaned.

The masked one spoke again in Russian and the Aeroflot woman said, "Take off your clothes, please."

Cayle stripped to his Y-fronts, but they made him take those off, too. The third woman, who was younger and prettier than the others, and seemed to be a nurse, looked down at him without interest. The one with the mask now took a stethoscope out of the bag and ran it over his chest. He flinched and grunted at appropriate intervals. She took his temperature, and spoke again to the Aeroflot woman, who told him: "It is necessary that you go to the hospital for examination."

He stared up at her in panic. "I can't! I'm flying to London today."

"It is not good that you travel," she said.

"Just give me something for the pain," he pleaded. "I'll be all right tomorrow."

There was a brisk discussion, then the woman doctor pulled off her mask and wrote something in a notebook, tearing off the page and giving it to the Aeroflot woman, who turned to Cayle and said, "I will send now for some medicine. You will please stay in this room. If you are not recovered by this afternoon, you will go to the hospital."

"What about my visa?" he asked feebly.

"You have visa valid how long?"

"I have to leave the Soviet Union tonight."

She nodded. "That will be arranged. Where is your passport?"

"Still with Reception." He sat up as the doctor and nurse started toward the door. "I don't want any trouble over my visa when I get to the airport!" he cried.

"There will be no trouble," said the Aeroflot woman placidly. "You will be given the necessary extension until you are able to travel." She turned, unsmiling, and the three of them walked out and closed the door.

Cayle waited a full hour before venturing along to the elevator and riding down to the subway station under the hotel, where he was safely lost among the mass of travelers from every part of the USSR. He took a train to Sverdlova Square, in the city center, and walked through driving snow to the Hotel Intourist, rising behind the Bolshoi like a huge upturned mouth organ.

The lobby was full of Western businessmen and the cool dry smell of air conditioning. The girl at the reception desk had mauve fingernails and an American accent. Cayle asked for Room 1727. She lifted a white telephone, whispered into it, and said to Cayle, "Your name please, sir?"

He told her, and she spoke again into the phone, then hung up. "The gentleman asks if you will meet him in the coffee lounge. He'll be down right away."

Cayle thanked her and bought a copy of yesterday's *Morning Star;* most of the front page was taken up with the threat of an engineering strike and a NATO build-up. Sir Roger Jameson-Clarke was squeezed into half an inch at the bottom of the inside page, under the headline NO CLUES TO MISSING FO MAN. It was a straight agency story and added nothing to what Cayle had last read on leaving London.

He walked up the shallow open stairway to the coffee lounge, and had just sat down at a corner table when a hand slapped him on the shoulder from behind. "Well, well, long time no see!" Lennie Maddox sat down opposite and bared his gums in greeting. "I called you a couple o' times, but they told me you'd gone back to the old country. Here for long?" he added.

"That depends."

"Depends on what?"

"I think you know that, Lennie. One of your mates among the Grey Men. The one who can't go back to his own country, because if he did they'd slam him in the clink for at least a hundred years. Unless someone killed him first, of course."

"Who's been talking about killing him?" said Maddox, pressing his knuckles against his damp chin.

"Just an idle thought. We journalists have a bad habit of always wanting to write the stories that never happen."

Maddox looked relieved. "By the way, how did you know I was here? You didn't ring, did you?"

"I came on spec, Lennie. Like I came back to Moscow on spec. I want to take you up on that deal."

Maddox's eyes flickered sideways. "One thousand dollars, U.S.," he murmured.

"It was five hundred last time," said Cayle.

"That was last time, Barry. I've got some more info since then. Something really big—and soon."

"I'm not horse-trading any more," said Cayle. "I'm in a hurry, too. So let's have a sample of what you've got."

There was a pause. Maddox seemed to be having difficulty getting comfortable on his chair. When he spoke, his eyes had a dull worried look. "Listen, things are coming to a head. That aircraft deal I told you about—well, they're holding a big reception for it tonight in the Kremlin. Pol's going to be one of the guests of honor. All the international press will be there—you, too, no doubt?" He looked expectantly at Cayle. "It'll be a good chance for you to meet Pol," he added.

"I'm not paying to meet Pol. I'm more interested in our other friend. The Grey One. I don't suppose you'd find him at a Kremlin reception."

"Don't worry!" Maddox pushed his face right up to Cayle's and whispered, "By tomorrow night I'll have the full gen for you. You won't be disappointed."

"Where and when do we meet?"

Maddox hesitated. "I don't even know where you're staying."

"The Aeroflot."

Maddox looked at his watch. "I'll call you there—between four and six tomorrow afternoon." He suddenly sounded anxious to leave. He stood up, and Cayle said:

"Anyway, I'll probably see you tomorrow night in the Kremlin?"

Maddox stopped and gave a cheerless laugh. "At a diplomatic reception? You must be joking! Or else you don't know much about dips. Hardly my social scene, old boy." He waved. "Till tomorrow evening—okay?"

"Okay," said Cayle; and he watched Maddox scuttle across the floor with his rusty head tilted to one side.

Some moments later a waitress sauntered across to take Cayle's order.

Charles Pol returned to his suite in the Hotel Intourist at just after five that evening. He bathed luxuriously, with a tumbler of Johnny Walker Black Label at his elbow; shaved and trimmed his goatee; sprinkled himself with Eau Sauvage; and with the help of a hand mirror arranged his remaining hair in an intricate spiral around the crown of his egg-shaped skull, signing it off with the black comma of kiss curl across his forehead. He then dressed in an outsize suit of white slub silk over a lace-frilled shirt and bold floral tie; and balancing his great weight on a pair of slipperlike shoes—the swelling in his right foot having greatly subsided—he confidently rang the Ministry and ordered a car for 7:30 to convey him to the Kremlin's Spasskye Gate.

The car arrived to the minute, and he was accorded an impressive ride into the ancient fortress of Russian power. Again the car's headlights were kept on high beam; the traffic lights at all the street intersections began flashing red at their approach; and militiamen stood holding back pedestrians with their lighted batons. They reduced speed only on the ramp up to the great gate in the crenelated wall behind its row of fir trees.

The two red lights on either side of the gate turned to amber, and a guard with an automatic rifle slung across the front of his long greatcoat stepped down and carefully inspected their credentials, saluted, and lifted a wall telephone. Instantly the twin lights turned to green and the iron gate swung soundlessly upward like a drawbridge, then slid shut behind them as they drove into the blue glare of an arc light. Two more guards, carrying only side arms this time, appeared from inside a bulletproof glass cubicle, studied the documents again, saluted, and a shrill bell began to ring.

It went on ringing as the car rumbled softly forward over a cobbled avenue, swept free of snow, between high walls of darkened windows, then into a courtyard ablaze with light and full of black official limousines, many of them with diplomatic number plates.

The car stopped, the door was pulled open, and Pol stepped out into an unnatural stillness. Boots creaked on the cobbles, and a couple of plain-clothes men escorted him through a pair of massive folding doors, into a vestibule where he was relieved of his vicuña coat and astrakhan hat, then ushered through another pair of doors into a long hall full of formally dressed men and women gripping glasses of champagne and talking in undertones.

From Pol's experience of Soviet government receptions, he knew that protocol not only controlled the rank of guest, but also extended to standards of behavior. Receptions given at Politburo level were always conducted with severe decorum—although lapses had been known. (Western Ambassadors had been insulted to their faces; top government officials had tried to lance the Gopek; and on a recent notorious occasion a member of the Central Committee had goosed the wife of a senior Scandinavian diplomat.)

Pol saw at once that the reception in his honor rated only second billing. The Central Committee was not represented, and most Western countries had sent only their First Secretaries or Heads of Chancery. On such occasions, the pace tended to be set by members of the foreign press corps; but it was early yet, and only the first tentative sips had been taken.

Pol succeeded finally in detaching himself from the row of formal greetings, and now made for the long white-covered table laden with regiments of bottles, plates of canapés, cream-layered cakes, caviar, fresh sturgeon, and giant pickled mushrooms. The most active of the waiters were elderly and discreetly efficient, like experienced croupiers, while behind them, standing like sentinels, stood rows of stocky pug-faced men in ill-fitting white jackets who rarely moved from their positions around the walls.

Pol noticed that as usual the women were conspicuously uninteresting, although it was clear that the Western wives had taken some trouble to paint and present themselves. The guests themselves were mostly still congealed in self-segregated groups from the various diplomatic colonies: there were the familiar black faces, dazed and docile, and little parties of awkward-looking brown and yellow men huddled together sipping sweet gassy lemonade. There were no Chinese.

Pol spotted his own Embassy delegation at the far end of the hall, surrounded by Russian dignitaries. Since the function was in honor of a nominally French enterprise, the Ambassador was present, together with all heads of departments; but Pol, who held diplomats in only slightly less contempt than politicians and policemen, was in no hurry to grant them the pleasure of his company.

One of the older waiters handed him a glass of champagne, which he recognized as Georgian, but tolerably dry this time. He helped himself to a plate of sturgeon and a pool of shiny grey Beluga, while all around him his Russian hosts lurked in surreptitious groups of twos and threes, choosing the people they talked to with obvious caution. Pol estimated them to be junior functionaries, interpreters, and informers.

At a few minutes past eight the Ministers of Trade, Transport, and Civil Aviation made their entrance, to an obsequious shuffling and bowing among the Soviet contingent. It was the signal for Pol to step reluctantly into the limelight.

The press had been among the last arrivals, distinguished by the speed with which they helped themselves to drinks and the way they moved, with weary indifference, among the various groupings about the hall. Barry Cayle came in the company of one of the less reputable members of the Western press corps, Frank Smollett, an angry little Irishman with red eyes and a beard like a hunk of Shredded Wheat.

Smollett was on his fourth cherry-vodka, and Cayle stood watching the guests, when there was a call for silence. A thin bespectacled man climbed onto the rostrum and began to speak into a microphone which at first failed to work. There were several whines and crackles, a piercing shriek, then a monotonous flow of Russian, followed by translations in French and English, to introduce the three Ministers. A burst of loud indifferent applause followed, then came the speeches.

The journalists stealthily refilled their glasses, since even the older waiters were now immobile. The thin man on the rostrum was translating a peroration about increased Franco-Soviet co-operation in the field of trade and technology when Cayle felt his pulse quicken with the dawning of great excitement. He was looking at the latest arrival at the party from the British Embassy—a short dapper man with glossy hair and small compact features. He nudged Smollett and pointed. "Know that little chap on the left?"

"Not personally. He's only been out here a few weeks."

"What's his name?"

"Why, d'you fancy him?"

"Come on, Frank, we all have to do our share of arse-licking. What's his name?"

"Hann. Simon Hann. With a name like that he should be running a bloody antique shop!" There was another burst of applause as Pol was hauled onto the rostrum and waddled up to the microphone, his silk suit shining like sharkskin under the chandeliers.

Cayle's interest was momentarily divided. Each of the Soviet Ministers stepped up and embraced Pol, their bodies swaying together like pairs of grotesque lovers. "What's his position, do you know?" said Cayle.

"Something to do with Chancery, I heard. Which means he's probably a spook." There was a ripple of polite laughter around the hall as Pol made a joke in bad Russian. He stood beaming down at his audience, his lips parted in an impish grin. Cayle lowered his voice and said, "I'd like to have a chat with this Hann. Can you introduce me?"

"I suppose so. I've nothing to lose but my sense of humor."

The British party consisted of three men, all of whom looked around with obvious distaste as Smollett approached. The First Secretary broke off what he was saying and gave an artificial smile. "Hello, Frank, enjoying the festivities?"

"A laugh a minute. You know Barry Cayle?"

"Yes, I think we all know Mr. Cayle, at least by reputation."

There was a heavy pause; then the Press Attaché, a fastidious little man called Giles, cleared his throat and said:

"I think, perhaps, there has been a failure of communication somewhere. A few days ago, Mr. Cayle, we were informed through London that the Soviet authorities had declared you *persona non grata.*"

Cayle chuckled. "Then there must, as you say, have been a failure in communication. Only why was London so interested? I mean, I know you still believe in looking after your ex-colonials, but I wouldn't want Whitehall to overwork themselves on my behalf." As he spoke, he glanced at Hann. Everything about him was statutory FO: pinstriped worsted suit with three tips of white handkerchief, flat gold cuff links, small square watch by Patek Phillipe. Only his eyes were remarkable; they were grey, cold, and oily. Cayle had seen the man before. He was certain of it now.

The First Secretary said, with a light laugh: "I'm quite sure that you can look after yourself. It's merely that as representative of a leading British newspaper, it could—as I'm sure you'll agree—be potentially embarrassing to Her Majesty's government if you were to find yourself in any difficulties with the Soviet authorities." He inclined his head. "But, of course, I speak as someone who is not privileged to know all the motives that your editor had in sending you to Moscow. This is your second visit in just over a week, isn't it?"

"Right."

"They're keeping you busy, Mr. Cayle." It was Hann who spoke, in a controlled, impassive voice. "What is it this time?" he added, with a discreet veneer of insult. "Another big in-depth exposé?"

Cayle stared over Hann's sleek head at the rostrum where Pol was pumping hands under the glare of flash bulbs. "I don't know about an exposé," he said, "unless you're thinking about something that happened a long time ago? About thirteen years ago, to be exact."

"I haven't the remotest idea what you're talking about, Mr.—I'm sorry, I didn't catch your name."

"Cayle. Barry Cayle." Bad move, he thought: professional diplomats don't forget names at official receptions. He smiled down at Hann's drink; it was a pale whisky. "Keeping off the vodka, eh, Mr. Hann? Very sensible! The real stuff can be pretty fierce. What someone we used to know in Beirut calls 'Russkie snakebite.' "

Hann didn't move; his eyes had that same dead oily look as when he'd marched Kim Philby out of the hotel bar in Beirut all those years back.

The First Secretary had turned to greet an elderly American couple, and Cayle heard Giles unctuously agreeing to make up a bridge party. Frank Smollett's glass was empty and he prowled away in search of a waiter. Cayle was alone with Hann.

"You didn't tell the truth just now, Mr. Cayle." There was no accusation in his voice; it was a statement of fact.

Cayle said nothing, and Hann continued: "I'd be interested to know, off the record, how you managed it. Slipping in without a visa, I mean. That sort of thing is rather difficult in Russia."

"A lot of things are more difficult in Russia than getting a legitimate three-day visa from Aeroflot when you're in transit."

"In transit for three days, eh?" Hann allowed himself a slight white smile. "And how did you manage to get yourself invited here?"

"That nice Madame Goncharova, at the Press Department of the Foreign Ministry—I called on her this afternoon and showed her a couple of letters, from my editor and my embassy in London, and hey presto! a lovely gilt-edged invitation."

"You're sailing pretty close to the wind, aren't you?" said Hann.

"I'd say we both were. Have you talked again to your fat chum up there yet?" He nodded toward the distant rostrum, where there was a dense crowd, still illuminated by the flash of cameras.

"One doesn't get a lot of time to talk to people at these sorts of functions," Hann said tonelessly. "What about you? Have you any particular interest in this Troika-Caravelle project?"

"I might have. Or, rather, somebody else thinks I might have."

Hann gave a little cough and put a finger to his old Harrovian tie. "It's rather crowded here. Let's try to find somewhere a little quieter." He began to lead Cayle toward the back of the hall, where there was a table with a stout copper samovar and a row of lacquered wooden mugs. He put down his glass of whisky and nodded gravely. "You're quite right about the drinking out here. It's not only a habit—it's an occupational hazard. The one thing the Russians can do well is tea." He pushed a wooden mug under the samovar spout, then paused. "You mentioned Beirut. The connection escapes me."

"It was eleven in the morning and Kim was resting on the bar. You came in and rescued him—rather too keenly, for my liking. None of us bothered that much about Kim's drinking. He had remarkable powers of recovery."

"Yes, he was very curious in that respect." Hann turned the tap of the samovar and the tea spurted out dark and boiling. He waited till the mug was a third full, then shut it off. "You said that somebody thought you might have an interest in this French deal. Would you mind telling me who it was?" He handed the tea to Cayle, then slid a second mug under the spout and jerked the handle again.

Cayle said: "An Englishman called Leonard Maddox. Works for Charles Pol. I expect you know him?"

"What makes you think I know either of them?" said Hann icily.

"Because Maddox told me you do—told me you met Pol up in the Lenin Hills a few weeks back."

"Maddox is a crook. Or didn't you know that?"

"Well, he's trying to flog me some info that he says he's got from Pol, and which involves you, among others. And he's asking for a thousand bucks, which he says is cheap at the price."

"I see." Hann gazed across the crowded hall where the listless diplomatic ritual was being resuscitated by a series of toasts. "But he hasn't yet told you what it is?"

"He's promised to call me before six tomorrow evening."

Hann winced as he sipped the scalding tea. "And you're prepared to do business?"

"I'm prepared to listen to what he's got to say."

"Yes, well that would be reasonable, under the circumstances. The trouble is, Mr. Cayle, you might also learn something that would put you in a highly sensitive position."

"I'll risk that," said Cayle. "You know, of course, what Maddox's going to tell me?"

Hann gave him a prim smile. "I suggest you let Maddox earn his thousand dollars. Though personally, I wouldn't trust him with a two-kopek piece."

"If he's a crook, why do the Russians put up with him? Or, for that matter, why does Pol?"

"Isn't there a proverb about letting the small fish catch the big fish? The Russians will pick him up in due course, and no doubt the Embassy will have to speak up in his favor."

"And you wouldn't like that?"

"It would be tiresome. People like Maddox always are. As for you, I advise you to treat anything Maddox tells you with a good measure of skepticism."

"I'm not a fool, Hann."

"I hope not." He flicked an invisible speck from his cuff and said, "Listen to what Maddox has to tell you tomorrow. It may be rubbish, but whatever it is, I'd like to know. And if you've got scruples about talking to me afterward, just remember that I know a lot more about this affair than either you or Maddox. I also have a lot more influence. You may be entering a very dangerous area, Cayle. I just hope, for your own sake, that you don't attempt to act alone."

He was interrupted by a small fat Russian who had been standing with a crowd some yards away, and who suddenly came cantering backward across the floor, cannoned off Hann's shoulder, splashing tea down the diplomat's trousers, and came to rest with a crash of glass against a double-glazed French window.

A waiter strolled over and kicked the glass under a curtain, but left the man where he was lying.

Hann had whisked the handkerchief out of his top pocket and was wiping down his trousers. "Drunken fool!" he muttered.

"Philby hates it, too," said Cayle. "In fact, he hates it so much, I've got an idea he'd like to get out, if he could."

"A journalist's pipe dream," said Hann. "Of course he can't. The Russians would never let him go. And anyway, even if they did, where would he go to?"

"A place in the sun where the drinks are cheap and the cops look the other way. A banana republic, probably."

Hann shook his head. "Too close to the CIA."

"Well, perhaps one of the Arab countries—one that isn't too tight on the booze."

"Too close to the Russians."

"And you think the Russians would go after him?"

Hann shrugged. "The British, the Americans, the Russians—what does it matter?"

"It would matter to Philby," said Cayle. "Or perhaps it wouldn't. Tell me something, Mr. Hann—what would you have done back in Beirut if you'd been in Kim's shoes?"

"God forbid. You tell me."

"I'd have kept a nice neat dossier, with all the names, dates, and details, on my former colleagues and accomplices in the FO and SIS, and perhaps a few other corners of the great British Establishment. And I'd have put that dossier in a Swiss bank, with instructions to a discreet Swiss lawyer for it to be published in the event of my arrest or violent death—including accidents."

Hann stepped away from him and said softly, "You're

even more naïve than I thought, Cayle. You're playing in Leonard Maddox's league now, and when things go wrong —as they're bound to go wrong—you're going to have no one to blame but yourself, and what's more, no one to help you."

Cayle leaned out and tapped the belly of the samovar. "It's just occurred to me—it might be a bit unfortunate if this conversation's been bugged?"

"It certainly would be," said Hann, "for you. I've got diplomatic immunity. Good night, Mr. Cayle. I may hear from you tomorrow?"

Cayle watched him walk away into the crowd.

The phone by his bed woke him at eight o'clock next morning. This time the line was clear, but the stammer had returned. "B-Barry? S-sorry to wake you so early, but you've been d-damned elusive. I c-called you f-five times last night."

"I was drinking champagne in the Kremlin," Cayle said sleepily. "By the way, is this line tapped?"

"Tapped b-both ends." There was a chuckle, then Philby went on: "I only heard yesterday that you're back with us." As his voice gained confidence, the stammer subsided. "You'll be checking out of your hotel today. And I want you to call round at four o'clock this afternoon to the travel bureau at the Hotel Intourist. Just show your passport, and you'll be given your ticket on the Red Arrow Express for Leningrad. You have a sleeper. It leaves at ten, and a driver will meet you in the lobby at nine-thirty to take you to the station."

"Who do I thank for this?" Cayle asked; and remembered his date to be at the Aeroflot Hotel before six, when Maddox would call.

Philby said: "A French gentleman called Pol. He's very

anxious that you and all your colleagues should be in Leningrad tomorrow for the inaugural flight of his new Troika-Caravelle airbus. I'm sure it'll make a couple of inches on page eight."

"You're very kind, said Cayle. "It was just what my editor had in mind. Any chance of us meeting again?"

"I'm sure there is. And, oh, Barry—" There was a pause, then another chuckle down the line. "Congratulations on your visa. I enjoyed that—especially your act with the doctors. What did you use? Cordite?"

"Soap."

"Must have been nice."

"Lovely. I just hope it pays off."

"Yes," said Philby, "so do I. By the way, you didn't b-by any chance b-b-"—again there was a pause—"bring me anything for my library?"

"Yeah, just a paperback this time. I expect you've got it—*The Heart of the Matter.*"

"Ah, wonderful book! His best, in my view. But it got him into a lot of trouble with his Catholic friends. It was even put on the Index. More censorship and suppression."

"How do I get it to you?" said Cayle.

"Oh, you can give it to me when we next meet."

"When will that be?"

"Soon, I hope. Well, 'bye for now. Enjoy Leningrad." And he hung up.

$$1 \quad 2 \quad 3 \quad 4 \quad 5 \quad \textcircled{6} \quad 7 \quad 8 \quad 9$$

$$10 \quad 11 \quad 12 \quad 13 \quad 14 \quad 15 \quad 16$$

*M. Pol stood at the window of his office on the* ninth floor of the Hotel Intourist and looked down on the evening glow of the city. He looked at the spray of lights at the entrance to the Bolshoi; the pricks of fluorescent blue around Revolution Square; at the four bright numerals of the illuminated digital clock over Karl Marx Prospekt. As he looked, the last numeral flicked from a 2 to a 3. It now read 1643. Pol consulted his watch and saw that it was running two minutes behind the electric sign below.

He turned slowly and said, "It is time you were departing, Monsieur Léonard."

Lennie Maddox glanced up from an electric typewriter on which he had been addressing envelopes for the past twenty minutes. *"Oui, Monsieur Pol."* His relations with his employer were cordial but correct; only occasionally, after a particularly arduous day's work or to celebrate some business coup, would Pol offer him a drink. But tonight Maddox was dismissed, with instructions to deliver an urgent message by hand to a room number in the Metropol before five o'clock.

Maddox had switched off the typewriter, and was arranging the finished envelopes into a neat pile when Pol said, "Leave them, Monsieur Léonard. You must hurry." There was an unfamiliar note of impatience in the Frenchman's voice, and he watched with a frown as Maddox pulled on his overcoat.

*"Au revoir, Monsieur Pol. A demain."*

Pol nodded and turned back to the window. The trams along Pushkin Street were packed; there were small crowds waiting for the lights at the corners of Gorki and Petrovska streets; and the digital clock above Karl Marx Prospekt now read 1645. Pol heard the door close softly behind Maddox. He waited till the digits changed to 46, then toddled over to the wall cabinet and poured himself an inch of whisky from a cut-glass decanter, sank into an armchair, and stared at his belly. "Man is driven by two forces," he reflected, "self-interest and fear." Both applied in classic measure to Leonard Maddox.

Maddox would be no loss to anyone, Pol decided. Unfortunately, however, it was not merely Maddox who presented the problem. For Maddox had a mistress in Moscow—an insufferably genteel Englishwoman whom Pol had carelessly neglected to find out about when he'd first employed Maddox. She had since become one of the small afflictions in the Frenchman's professional life, turning up uninvited at his office in the Hotel Intourist, where she was always trying to tempt him with what she claimed was inside information on commodities.

Pol had discovered that she had a part-time job with the English-language section of Radio Moscow, and that she lived with Maddox in a block of flats reserved for foreigners. Maddox had also told him that she'd had experience in a London finance house, and it was clear to Pol that she had ambitions toward being taken on by Entreprises Lipp. These he had so far firmly resisted.

As for Lennie Maddox, he'd been recommended to Pol by a financier in Geneva who'd assured him that the Englishman had a sharp head for figures and could be relied upon not to be too scrupulous about Pol's more delicate dealings, provided the money was right; and besides, Maddox had had the advantage of appearing so immediately untrustworthy that should any serious complications have ever arisen with the Soviet authorities, he would have made an obvious scapegoat.

Pol had paid him a comfortable salary in Swiss francs, transferred monthly to Moscow, plus the promise of a bonus when his year's contract had expired. That contract still had just over seven months to run; and Pol had thought it would be enough to keep Maddox satisfied, without making him greedy. He'd been wrong.

Pol hated to be wrong. It made him reckless and vengeful; and he just hoped that he had not let his emotions distort his judgment; that his hasty arrangements for the evening would prove satisfactory. But even then, only half the problem would be solved. The other half was Maddox's damnable lady-friend. For over the last few days there had been certain developments that had convinced Pol that Lennie Maddox was not just greedy and treacherous; he was also stupid. By a stroke of extreme luck, involving the Englishwoman's infidelity to her lover, Pol had learned that Maddox had not only been stealing confidential information, but that he had also discussed at least some of this information with his mistress.

The knowledge that anyone—let alone a pair of cheap Anglo-Saxon chiselers with the morals of alley cats—should know anything about his private affairs caused Pol not merely embarrassment, but also, in this case, grave concern.

He sipped his Scotch and felt some of the tension seeping out of his massive frame, when the telephone purred on the desk. A man's voice, with a thick accent, said in French: "Your reservation to Leningrad is being con-

firmed, Monsieur. I will call you as soon as it is in order."
Pol thanked him and hung up. His watch now said
eleven minutes to five. Two minutes slow, by the sign
over Karl Marx Prospekt. He would check it by the time
signal at five on the radio.

Six o'clock, he thought. He should know by then—know
enough to be safe. He finished his drink, made sure that
all the drawers in the filing cabinet were locked, paused
at the desk and flicked through the envelopes that Maddox had been addressing—noting what a slovenly typist
he was—then looked again at his watch. The minute hand
in the chunky platinum case seemed scarcely to have
moved. Platinum, he thought: that's what Maddox's mistress had been going on about last night—sitting there on
his desk and telling him how to corner the platinum
market. Impertinent camel! But with any luck she
wouldn't be troubling him any more.

He returned to the window. It was not in his nature to
be pessimistic, but here the timing had to be exact, and
yet so many things had been left to chance. Like all the
elevators being taken and Maddox having to use the
stairs; the possibility of his stopping to buy cigarettes—
but then, he didn't smoke, of course. Or running into a
friend, or dropping into the bar.

No, he thought. His instructions had been imperative
—the message must be delivered at the Metropol *before*
five o'clock.

It was only a few minutes' walk from the Hotel Intourist to the Metropol, even allowing for the rush-hour
traffic. It had stopped snowing, but the ground was treacherous, with the powdered surface trampled into black
ice, and banks of sludge piled up at the edge of the gutters
where the snowplows had passed.

Lennie Maddox crossed Pushkin Street and felt the chill of the evening, even through his fur-lined overcoat. He had a funny feeling—a funny itchy feeling in his legs and up the base of his spine that made him want to quicken his steps, break into a run. But it was no feeling of elation. He wanted to get away. Get away from Pol, from Moscow, even from Joyce. It had become a stinking business. And in the end Joyce had betrayed him, just as he had betrayed—or was about to betray—Pol. It was time to cut his losses and get out.

At the corner of broad Karl Marx Prospekt where it opens into Revolution Square he joined the crowd waiting for the lights to change. A militiaman stood in the center of the Prospekt and executed heavy-footed pirouettes, swinging his lighted baton for the traffic to move or stop. A man bumped against Maddox and mumbled something, dropping a box of matches in the snow. He leaned down and fumbled for it with his woolen mittens, failed to retrieve it, and lurched out into the street. A car hooted, there was a screech of brakes, the man groped backward, tripped on the curb and sat down in the slush. The pedestrian signal lights changed to green and the crowd began to move around him.

There was a shrill whistle blast and the militiaman came striding over, yelling furiously. Several of the crowd stopped to watch. The man sat cross-eyed in the snow and made a helpless gesture with his mittened hand. The militiaman seized his arm and tried to yank him to his feet. An old woman in a man's overcoat waded in and began to shout at the militiaman, who let go of the man's arm to defend himself against the woman's fury.

The crowd was now drifting back across the Prospekt. Maddox wished he'd had his camera. The scene would have made a good pic—typical vignette of Moscow life, the sort of thing the posh Sunday papers went in for—Cayle's paper, for instance. He was thinking about Cayle when the truck hit him.

There was no horn, no sound of brakes or slither of tires; it hit him side on, the high steel bumper scooping him off the ground and flinging him up to where the pointed radiator grille snapped his spine and sent his body hurtling forward, twisting in mid-air and flopping down on the black ice just as the front wheel crushed his neck, almost severing it from his body. The double rear wheels followed, smashing his shoulders and splitting his head open like a soft-boiled egg.

It was over in three seconds. The truck accelerated with a skidding howl and turned sharply left into Revolution Square, cut across a taxi, which had to brake to a halt, then, with a burst of black exhaust smoke, which obscured its rear number plate, it raced down Petrovska Street and disappeared behind the Bolshoi.

The digital clock above Karl Marx Prospekt flicked to 1646.

Pol watched the crowd swelling at the corner by the lights. The militiaman was struggling to hold them back; traffic began piling up; more people were swarming across from the Square. A mobile police patrol would arrive any moment; and the ambulance would not be much longer. Where accidents were concerned, Moscow was an efficient city.

He finished his second whisky, waddled into the bathroom, and turned the taps on full. He was sweating, and cursed the hotel for not having separate central-heating regulators in all rooms. For a man like Pol, one of the few luxuries of Moscow in winter was that he didn't have to sweat too much. Until now.

He was lowering himself into the bath when the phone rang again. With surprising agility he sprang out and paddled back, naked and dripping, into the main room, where he wiped his hand on a cushion before lifting the receiver. The same man spoke again in French: "Monsieur Pol?" Pol grunted, and the voice said, "All is in order, monsieur. Your ticket and reservation have been confirmed."

"You are absolutely sure?"

"Absolutely. Thank you."

"Thank you," said Pol, and he hung up smiling. His smile became a cooing chuckle as he poured himself a third whisky, larger this time, and carried it back into the bathroom. He could relax now. There was plenty of time before the car came to collect him.

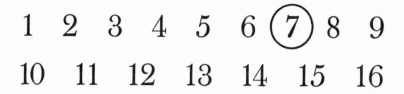

*When Cayle checked out of the Aeroflot Hotel* that morning he learned that his bill had been settled. He did not inquire by whom; that would only attract attention. Instead he asked the girl at Reception to tell anyone who called that he would be back by five o'clock. He lunched at the Foreign Press Club and, glancing through yesterday's Western papers, saw that the only development over the disappearance of Sir Roger Jameson-Clarke had been a question in the Commons, asking the Home Secretary when Sir Roger had last had a security vetting, and what results had been. The written reply had stated that all Foreign Office personnel were subject to the same Security controls, and that the Home Secretary was satisfied that these controls were perfectly adequate, without being obtrusive. Meanwhile, Sir Roger was still missing.

At four o'clock Cayle went to the travel bureau on the first floor of the Hotel Intourist and collected an envelope with his name typed across the front and containing a first-class sleeper reservation on the Red Arrow Express to Leningrad that night. On his way out he looked into the bar, the two restaurants, and the coffee lounge, to see if there was any sign of Maddox; then took a taxi back to the Aeroflot, where he was told that there had been no messages for him.

He spent the next three hours drinking tea and Russian beer, and reading a free pamphlet entitled *Progressive*

*Culture in the German Democratic Republic* over a dinner of borscht, pirotchki, and beetroot. He also checked every half hour at the desk to see if Maddox had called. He had not.

At nine that evening Cayle left the Aeroflot Hotel for the last time; and half an hour later returned to the Hotel Intourist, where he was half tempted to call Room 1727; but an instinct warned him not to force the pace. Instead, he went to the Beriozka, the foreign-currency shop, where he bought a half-liter bottle of Osoboya vodka for the journey. Next to him a group of young Americans were discussing a road accident near the Bolshoi. Cayle gathered that the victim had been a Westerner, killed outright by a hit-and-run driver. He went out to the lobby and asked one of the girls at Reception about it; she said she'd heard something, but did not know the details.

Ten minutes later, punctually at 9:30, his car arrived. The driver was an old man with a face like broken rock, who drove out into the traffic without looking to left or right. Cayle kept his eyes closed for most of the journey, until they stopped at a low ill-lit building with a damp red slogan draped across the entrance, and a bleak ticket-office area littered with cigarette butts and squashed paper cups. A very pretty girl with apple cheeks surrounded by a halo of white fur was licking ice cream by the refreshment kiosk. Otherwise there were few people about.

Cayle's driver insisted on carrying his suitcase through the barrier, despite the fact that he had a bad leg. The platforms were in the open, covered only by well-trampled snow. The train had not yet arrived. The old man had taken charge of Cayle's ticket, and, after pondering over the reservation slip, began limping up the platform, counting his footsteps aloud to himself; he finally stopped and gave Cayle a steel-toothed grin. Cayle tried to pay him, but he shook his head vigorously and asked for an American cigarette. Cayle gave him a cheroot instead, took one for himself, lit them both, and the two of them stood alone on the platform, puffing in silence.

Cayle wanted to return to the station for a beer, and perhaps another look at the pretty girl in the white fur hat; but when he made a move, the old man grabbed his arm and started a garbled speech in Russian in which the words *"stally mattoo!"* were repeated several times, while he kicked his good leg savagely at the snow. It was only when he mentioned the word *"futbul"* that Cayle realized he had been talking about Stanley Matthews. He didn't look like routine KGB material, but he was certainly determined that Cayle should catch the train.

Cayle threw away the stub of his cheroot and was stamping his feet with cold when he saw the girl in white fur coming down the platform toward them, carrying a large battered suitcase. She stopped a few yards away, sat down on the suitcase, and lit a cigarette. A few minutes later there was a low moan, and a bright red eye crept toward them out of the darkness.

The train's wide-gauge carriages were dark and solid, with wheels of polished iron, windows drawn with white lace curtains, the roofs glistening with fresh snow. It clanked to a halt, and Cayle now saw why the old man had been counting his steps. The door of the first-class compartment whose number corresponded with the one on Cayle's reservation slip had stopped opposite them.

Again the old man insisted on lugging his suitcase aboard, down the varnished corridor to a compartment with four bunks. He checked Cayle's reservation again, then lifted the lower bunk and was fitting his luggage inside when Cayle saw the girl standing in the corridor outside, holding her suitcase in both hands.

The old man straightened up and seized Cayle in a brutal handshake, then turned and pushed past the girl and disappeared down the corridor. Cayle stepped forward and said, "Please!" in Russian. She responded with a bright smile as he took hold of her suitcase. He had begun to carry it along the corridor when she directed him back into the compartment, pointing at the lower bunk opposite his own.

"Thank you, sir," she said in English, with an accent so pure that it was almost affected, except for the broad Russian vowels. "You are English, yes?" she added. "Or perhaps you are from America?"

"From Australia," he said.

"Yes, but that is like English, I think, because you have the same Queen?" She giggled and threw her white fur hat down on the bunk and began unbuttoning her long woolen coat.

Cayle helped her off with it, noticing that she was small and plump, with a fringe of dark-brown hair above wide matching eyes. She sat down on the bank opposite him, smoothed her dress over her knees and said, "I am Galina Valisova. I am pleased to meet you." They shook hands across the floor, and Cayle told her his name.

"Cay-eel? I have not heard such a name before," she said, and stared at the teak-and-mahogany wall, with its brass fittings and little red lampshades over each bunk. "Did you perhaps see the *Fwarsite Saga* on your BBC television?" she said suddenly.

"I think I saw a couple of episodes," Cayle said, slightly confused.

She nodded. "I watched all the episodes except the last one, when my mother was sick. They were beautiful and most interesting. Do you smoke?"

"Only these, I'm afraid," he said, bringing out his depleted packet of cheroots.

"No," she said. "Please do not smoke them in here. They make a bad smell."

He put them away in his pocket and wondered what the next gambit would be. He decided to take the initiative, and got the bottle of Osoboya vodka out of his suitcase under the bunk. He sat down again and had finished peeling the foil cap off the top of the bottle when she said, "You like vodka?"

"It's great for the cold," he replied, with an uneasy grin. "And this is the best vodka in the world."

She shook her head. "I do not like vodka. It makes people go crazy."

He looked at her glumly, wishing he'd bought some Georgian champagne instead. "The trouble is, I haven't got a cork for it," he said at last. "And I can't just throw it away, can I?"

"You will drink it all only when I am asleep," she said firmly, then unsnapped the catches of the suitcase beside her and, after rummaging under a pile of clothes, pulled out a wad of coarse cotton wool. "This is your 'quark'!" she cried gleefully as she grabbed the bottle out of his hand, screwed a tuft of wool into the neck, stood up, and placed it on the table under the window.

"You know Swir Valter Squat?" she added.

"You mean Walter Scott?"

"Yes, Squat." She smiled. "I do not say it very well?"

Just then the door slid open and a young man with a thin beard came in carrying a rucksack. He stood for a moment in the doorway studying his ticket and the two upper bunks, then mumbled something in Russian and slung his rucksack onto the bunk above the girl's head. He was wearing a windbreaker over a denim track-suit with the inverted Y sign of the Campaign for Nuclear Disarmament printed in white across his chest.

The girl was saying, "I like very much this Squat. His books are very historic and interesting."

The young man said, "You both speak English?"

"Yes, we do," said the girl.

"That's great. I haven't spoken English for six weeks. I'm American," he added. "Don Passmore. Glad to meet you both."

"I am Galina Valisova," the girl said, leaping up and grabbing the American's limp hand. Cayle just nodded. Galina was now showing Passmore where the stepladder was folded under the table.

"Thanks," said Passmore, propping it against his bunk and testing it for strength. He was very thin. "I started off from San Francisco to Yokohama two months ago," he added, "and got sick in Vladivostok. Acute hepatitis. I was in the hospital there for six weeks. I was real sick."

"They look after you well in Soviet hospitals," said Galina Valisova.

"Yeah, well." He started awkwardly up the ladder. "I didn't have to pay anything. Only as soon as I was well enough to get out of bed, they made me help clean up the ward." He climbed onto his bunk and began arranging his blankets and pillow. "I guess we undress when the train gets started and they turn the lights down?" he added.

Galina Valisova laughed. "You can undress now. It does not matter." As she spoke, the door opened again and a porter struggled in with two large white leather suitcases and a wicker basket covered with a napkin. He was followed by Charles Pol, who was only just able to squeeze through the open door, swathed in soft heavy vicuña. *"Je m'excuse,"* he muttered, and glanced up at the bunk above Cayle's. *"Ah, merde!"*

"Can I help you?" Cayle said in French.

"Thank you. It is only that I am not, as you see, very athletic." Pol grinned and began to haul off his vicuña coat, while Cayle stood up to let the porter stow the two suitcases under the bunk.

Reluctantly, because it would place him out of easy reach of Miss Galina Valisova, Cayle surrendered his lower bunk to the Frenchman, who bowed with a creak of silk and thrust out a fat pink hand with fingers like fresh-peeled shrimps. *"Merci, monsieur. Je suis Charles Pol. Enchanté."*

"I am Barry Cayle," Cayle replied, still in French; then added, poker-faced: "I do not think that you require my passport details?"

Pol moved his hands in a gesture of Gallic delicacy. "No, it is not necessary, Monsieur Cayle. In Moscow one has so few secrets." He winked and took Cayle's arm in a surprisingly firm grip. "I regret the inconvenience," he murmured.

"It is no matter. I expect I would have slept badly anyway."

Pol lifted an eyebrow. "You always sleep badly on trains? You should have gone by air, my friend."

Cayle smiled. "Yes, I should have gone by air. But as you know, Monsieur Pol, it is so much easier to become acquainted on a train than an airplane."

Pol patted his elbow and said, "We will talk later.

There will be plenty of time before we reach"—he chuckled—"St. Petersburg."

Someone came down the corridor clanking a hand bell. Galina Valisova jumped up and cried, "That is the samovar lady! You would like samovar?" she asked Cayle.

"You have samovar," he said; "I prefer something stronger." He saw her frown disapprovingly as he unplugged the cotton wool from the vodka bottle and took a swift drink. At the same moment, Passmore's pale face peered down from the top bunk and he called: "Could someone get me a glass of water, please? I feel kinda tired after climbing up here."

Galina Valisova nodded and skipped out into the corridor. Cayle offered the Osoboya to Pol, who stayed his hand. "I have something rather more special, my friend." He leaned down, almost splitting the back of his jacket, and lifted the napkin off the basket on the floor. Underneath was the slim neck of a magnum of Dom Perignon standing in an ice bucket, with four tulip glasses tucked into the corners.

Galina Valisova had returned with a steaming glass of tea in a silver filigree holder, and a paper cup of water, which she handed up to Passmore. He thanked her with a weary nod and lay back on his pillow. Galina Valisova now saw the champagne and gave a squeak of excitement. "It is real champagne? French champagne?" she cried, and touched both hands together as though in prayer.

Pol said, "It is the only champagne," and began easing out the cork.

Galina Valisova left her tea on the floor, and began jumping up and down in her little sealskin boots, her plain black dress discreetly concealing her plump calves. Pol had just popped the cork and caught the froth skillfully in her glass when there was a jolt and they began to move.

They touched glasses and drank to the journey ahead. Cayle was watching Galina Valisova carefully, unable to make out whether she spoke French or not. She drank her champagne as though it were lemonade, and Pol gave a little clucking noise like a hen each time he refilled her glass. "I should have brought a whole crate!" he cried. Galina Valisova smiled and drank.

By the time the overhead light was turned off, the magnum was empty. Galina Valisova was stretched out fully clothed on her bunk, with her face lit up in a circle of pink light from the red-shaded reading lamp. Above her, Passmore was taking advantage of the dark to get undressed. Cayle nodded to Pol, with a glance at the girl, and they both moved out into the corridor.

"Very chic," said Cayle.

"You mean the little one?"

"I mean the whole operation. Chic and competent," Cayle said, still in French.

Pol wedged his toes and shoulders against the swaying sides of the corridor. "I am pleased that you appreciate it, my friend."

"Can we speak English?" said Cayle.

"My English is not good," Pol said.

"That's fine. It'll give me the advantage."

Pol nodded slowly, watching the squares of light rippling across the snow outside. "You have many advantages in this country, Monsieur Cayle," he said, in English.

"Only I seem to be depending too much on too many people. And none of them are my employers in London."

Pol shunted his colossal buttocks down the mahogany wall and gave a noisy belch. *"Ah, merde!* Champagne and

whisky—it never agrees with me. One of the great trage-
dies of life, I find, is that the older one gets, the greater
become one's appetites."

"When I first got to Moscow," said Cayle, "someone
told me you were a Marxist."

Pol giggled. "Not a Russian, I hope. No, the Russian
authorities have a deep and sensible distrust of Western
businessmen with Utopian ideals."

"It was an Englishman," said Cayle; he was watching
closely for Pol's reactions, but observed none. "Someone
I met on the plane from London. It may have been a coincidence. But since then he's been showing a great deal
of interest in me."

"Interest?"

"He's been trying to sell me a story. A story that was
going to cost my newspaper five thousand dollars."

"It must be a very good story," Pol murmured, "or the
man is an idiot."

"You're in the best position to judge that," said Cayle.

"*Comment?*" Pol gave him an innocent stare.

Cayle hesitated; then decided that he owed no special
loyalty to Leonard Maddox. "The man works for you—or
claims to. Little fellow called Maddox."

Pol sunk his chin into the voluminous folds of his silk
cravat. "Did you accept his offer?"

"No."

"Why not?"

"I didn't have the chance. He was supposed to call me
this evening at my hotel, and didn't. He promised to tell
me something. Something about a fellow-Englishman living here in Moscow." He glanced up and down the corridor. They were alone except for a man in a vest shaving
with an electric razor. "An Englishman who could mean
bad trouble, Monsieur Pol."

"Trouble?"

"The man is considered in his own country to be a major criminal. A traitor."

"Traitor?" Pol repeated. "It is a useless word. Who are the great traitors? Pétain? Salan? De Gaulle? Perhaps your Mister Smith in Rhodesia?" He gave a massive shrug and stood gripping the brass rail under the window. Cayle said nothing.

"Things have been arranged for you in Leningrad," Pol went on. "There, I promise you, you will find a most amusing story for your newspaper. What is more, it will not cost you a centime."

"That's nice of you. But what happens to poor Maddox and his five thousand dollars?"

"Bah! Maddox was an idiot, he was not serious. He was also as bent as a mountain road, though he had his uses, I admit."

*"Was?"* said Cayle.

*"Quoi?"* Pol was staring out the window, his great body absorbing the rhythm of the train, and Cayle could still detect no concern in his face, except that he had begun to sweat.

"You spoke of Maddox in the past tense, Monsieur Pol. What's happened to him?"

Pol turned and gave him a quick warning glance. A couple of large men in open shirts were swaying down the corridor toward them, carrying soap and towels. Pol waited until they had struggled past him, then said: "My dealings with Monsieur Maddox have always been of a strictly business nature. They are therefore confidential."

"I think that Maddox was trying to peddle information not only to me—he was also passing it to British Intelligence."

"You have proof of this?"

"Just an inspired guess. Somehow he found out I was coming to Moscow—or was told by someone—and managed to get a seat on the same plane. He also made it clear that first evening that he knew I'd come over to see Philby."

Pol touched a forefinger to his cherry lips. "Sh! Here we talk only of Monsieur Kim. Never his family name, please!" He leaned back and closed his eyes again, his pink domed forehead now bright with sweat. "I confess that Monsieur Maddox has been a great problem to me," he added. "But now the matter is happily terminated."

Cayle grinned. "Terminated with extreme prejudice?"

"Eh?"

"It's a favorite expression of the CIA's. As you would say, 'regler son compte.' Kill somebody."

Pol sighed. "You are a very presumptuous man, Monsieur Cayle. But, of course, in your profession you are accustomed to making presumptions, no doubt? However, you are also a man who speaks his mind, and, fortunately for you, that is something I appreciate. But perhaps I may also offer you a word of advice. It is always wise to temper directness with discretion."

"Thank you. But I'm going to leave that advice for the moment, and ask you a very indiscreet question."

Pol chuckled. "My dear friend, there are never indiscreet questions, only indiscreet answers."

"Fine. Now let's get things straight. We're in this together—both involved with Monsieur Kim—only for different motives. Mine is to get a newspaper story. What's yours?"

"Ah!" Pol gaped at him with mock outrage. "Now that *is* an indiscreet question. However, I think I can trust you enough to answer it. When you ask me what is my motive in this affair, I can only reply that it is the oldest in the world. Also the most vulgar. Money."

"So Maddox was wrong when he said you were an idealist?"

"Maddox was a *misérable*. He saw nothing beyond his nose. But you must understand, *mon cher*, that whatever the moralists say, ultimately everything of value in this life—including ideals—must be related to hard currency."

"And who's providing it this time? Surely somebody very interested in Monsieur Kim's fate. And I don't suppose *he's* got the kind of money you'd be interested in— even if you considered rubles to be hard currency."

"What are you implying, Monsieur Cayle?"

"If they were pushed, the British Secret Service might have the right money. They've certainly still got an interest in Monsieur Kim."

Pol made a little growling noise and spat delicately between his feet. "I'm afraid that again you are asking indiscreet questions, Monsieur Cayle. The matter of my personal finances is no concern of yours. Now, I am tired." He sighed and nodded at their compartment door. "The little one will now have finished her toilette, I think."

"Who is she?" said Cayle.

"Ah! A little idea of Monsieur Kim's," he cooed, "to keep you company in Leningrad!" And he turned and pulled open the compartment door.

Galina Valisova now lay tucked into her bunk, her wide dark eyes peeping out above the sheet, while Passmore's voice droned down from the bunk above: "You people are going to encounter the same sociological problems, however good your organization is. You see, it's organization that is the real problem."

"Rwoot?" she called up; then looked around smiling as

Pol and Cayle came in and sat down opposite her on Pol's bunk. "Mr. Passmore has been informing me," she said, "of many interesting facts about the American society. It is very complicated."

Cayle groped out in the dark for the bottle of Osoboya on the table under the window. "Has he told you about the new CIA computer?" he asked. "The one that can translate *Gone With the Wind* into Russian in twenty minutes?"

"Aw, for God's sake," Passmore cried feebly, "don't go bring the CIA into this!"

Cayle watched Galina Valisova's naked shoulders creep an inch above the sheet. He pulled the cotton plug out of the bottle, took a swallow, and passed it to Pol. "Mr. Passmore doesn't like me talking about the CIA, Galina. It's a very sensitive subject for Americans. It's the equivalent of the KGB," he added, as Pol again belched noisily beside him.

"Lay off," said Passmore. "It isn't the same thing at all. The KGB is for internal security—like the American NSA, the National Security Agency."

In the darkness Pol made a slow retching noise, while the American went on, like a late-night radio announcer: "But the CIA is a highly motivated government-within-a-government. Its budget is more than many small countries' put together. It's a force for evil," he said as Pol vomited between his knees.

"*Ah, merde!*" he growled, and Cayle felt the bunk lurch upward as the Frenchman's weight lifted and he lunged for the door.

Cayle saw Galina's head duck back under the sheet, and he was just in time to drag the door open and push Pol out into the corridor before he was sick again.

"*Whiskey et le champagne,*" he groaned.

"Followed by vodka," Cayle said brutally. "Poison." He grabbed the Frenchman under the armpits and they began to stumble forward, Pol bouncing off the compartment doors with his head down, hands clasped across his mouth.

The door of the toilet opened into a small room with a kidney-shaped sofa in wine-red velvet and a long gilded mirror under a tasseled lamp. The lavatory was through a second door. Both rooms were unoccupied, and Cayle managed to haul Pol through the two doors and push his head down into the toilet. The Frenchman's big shiny face had turned the color of a mushroom, and his spiral of black hair was spread across his egg-shaped head like a damp spider.

Cayle went back and locked the outer door. Pol was now on his knees, grasping the lavatory bowl with both hands. "Who's Passmore?" Cayle shouted, above the roar of the wheels.

"Passmore?" Pol muttered, and his body heaved forward. "I don't know him. He's just an American—an ordinary American."

Cayle tore out a paper towel from beside the basin, ran some cold water, and began to sponge the back of Pol's neck. The Frenchman slowly struggled to his feet, and Cayle guided him to the basin. There were faint blotches of color on his cheeks, but his eyes were tiny and dilated like dull beads. "My stomach," he moaned. "Ah, my stomach—it is ruined."

A voice bellowed something in Russian through the outside door, and the handle rattled violently. Cayle yelled, "Okay—*harasho!* Are you feeling better now?" he said to Pol.

The Frenchman turned and spat into the basin. There now came a heavy pounding on the outer door, followed by a kick. Cayle began to get angry. Pol was being sick again, this time into the basin, and Cayle left him and went through to the outer door. He snapped the lock up, pulled the door open, and had said the first syllable of the only Russian obscenity he knew when he was hit. It was a quick hard blow on the side of his neck, and as he stumbled, a gloved fist smashed into his jaw. He felt his head crack against the doorjamb, and caught a glimpse of two men, thickset, in dark overcoats and black fur caps. He tried to back away and get the door shut again, but lost consciousness first.

It returned in dull, disjointed waves. The floor was grinding and clanking, then falling away under him: the blue night-lights along the corridor roof came on bright again: he had the sensation of being lifted, dragged, his feet thumping down metal steps: a blast of freezing air and somewhere a voice saying, "Fuck, it's that bastard, Cayle!"

His legs were knee-deep in snow. He saw the train lit up in a long caterpillar of light. A bell was ringing. His arms were held stiff at his sides, and he was being dragged backward, and the snow felt light and spongy under his feet. A whistle blew, and a voice called, "For Christ's sake, hurry!"

He felt dry leather and a sudden warmth. His trouser legs began dripping melted snow. He was in the back of a car. The engine was running and there was the blast of a fan heater. Two men got in, one in front and one beside him, and the car sprang forward. A white glare swept across a high bank of snow and the straight black stems of pine trees. The driver called over his shoulder, "Keep a good eye on him. Hit him again if he moves."

Cayle didn't move, except to be slung from side to side,

bumping up and down as the headlights flashed across the white-laced trees, plunging down into hollows of darkness. Sometimes he caught a glimpse of the man beside him: his face a dark blur under the fur hat, which had the ear flaps hanging loose, swaying with the motion of the car.

From the front seat came a small red glow as the driver touched the dashboard lighter to a cigarette. He drew on it and the glow lit up his hard lumpy complexion. Like cold porridge, thought Cayle. Then he blacked out again.

# 1 2 3 4 5 6 7 ⑧ 9
# 10 11 12 13 14 15 16

*It was still too early for the tourist season, and* the resort of Gagra, with its elegant palm-fringed front curving along the margin of the Black Sea, was quiet and empty in the southern spring. Most of the hotels were closed, the ice-cream emporiums shuttered, the chess sets locked away in the beach huts, the skiffs and pedalos pulled up on the pebbled shore.

The day had been unusually warm, even for Georgia, and when Joyce Warburton had stepped off the train from Sochi that afternoon she had not even needed her coat. The orange trees along the main boulevard were not yet in blossom, and the snow line had been clear and very close, suspended high above the houses like a reef of shining cloud.

As usual, the arrangements had been immaculate: there had been a car to meet her and drive her to the Grand Hotel Gagra, where she had been shown into a suite over-looking the sea. She had had little unpacking to do—an evening dress, pair of shoes, and change of underwear, and her few toilet things, which had looked rather pathetic spread out on the huge naked dressing table. The tired trappings of the dirty weekend—in Leningrad, Kiev, Yalta, Sochi, and now Gagra. Only this time she had been promised that it would be different. From now on, no more excuses, no more brave smiles when she greeted Lennie Maddox back at the flat on Sunday evening, having to endure his simpering smile, his sudden tantrums and table-thumping rages. He was a vulgar bully; it had shown in his love-making, aggressive and artless, and in his treatment of waiters, clerks, cloakroom attendants—people he'd been able to lord it over in the West, but who shrugged him off in the Soviet Union, regarding him as just another ugly little foreigner.

That's just what he was, she thought: ugly and little. A nobody—so that now it was as though he'd never existed. Occasionally, over the last twenty-four hours, since she'd been offered her freedom, she had been surprised, even a little dismayed at her complete lack of feeling for him. She told herself that she'd stuck him for so long because she'd thought he might be useful to her—at least, while he stayed with the Frenchman, for it had always seemed there might be some rich crumbs from that table. And besides, he had looked after her, provided for her, taken her out and shown her off—the best tables in the top Moscow restaurants, seats at the Bolshoi, the ritual round of cocktail parties and receptions where she'd been able to flirt skittishly with glassy-eyed diplomats and bored businessmen.

At first, the few shreds of English suburban tact that had clung to her as far as Moscow had prevented her from being unfaithful to Lennie; but soon there had been that glamorous photographer who was part Lebanese and had broken with his wife; but that hadn't stopped him from returning to Rome after only six weeks, and since then there had been only one postcard.

Then the Englishman had come along.

She'd met him at a rather dull dinner party given by a Russian whom Lennie had described as being "something pretty big with the KGB," and who in turn seemed to believe that Lennie was equally big with Entreprises Lipp. It had been a typically ghastly evening, she remembered, with the Russians insisting on setting fire to their vodkas before drinking them, with the result that many of them had badly burned their mouths; and with one KGB man, who had gone outside to get some air, disappearing down an open manhole and breaking his hip.

During all this, she had found herself seated between an elderly Englishman and a Russian who spoke no English, and who had been counted out in the early stages of the meal when his head had slumped into his soup and had been pulled out just in time to save him from drowning. For the rest of dinner she had the Englishman to herself. She had been a trifle disconcerted when he introduced himself as "Kim" Philby: though not so much by his reputation as by his obvious gentleness. She could not believe that he could really be a villain—or, for that matter, a Hero of the Soviet Union. While she was flattered and excited by the attentions of such a man, what really attracted her was something sad, almost defenseless, about him, with his poor tired face and that terrible stammer. He'd been through so much. A lone wolf come home to die was how he'd described himself. And that's what she'd come to call him: "Lone Grey Wolf." And in turn he had called her his "Golden Mouse," on account of her pale russet hair, which owed more to a hairdresser in Copenhagen than to nature; and whenever he called her by this pet name it made her feel just like a schoolgirl again.

In fact, she had been smitten like a schoolgirl from that very first meeting. (Only later had she heard the rumors that his long liaison with Melinda Maclean had just ended.) The next day he had telephoned her at the flat, while Lennie was at the office, and there began a number of discreet meetings, in cafés, obscure restaurants, museums and theaters, and walks through the city parks. Then, after a decent interval of three weeks, he had seduced her, rather uncomfortably, on the back seat of an old Moskvitch car during an excursion into the Lenin Hills.

Through the whole idyllic winter that followed she had indulged her secret passion, with each of them playing a protracted game of lovers in a hostile land—she outwitting the sly suspicions of Lennie Maddox, and he ducking the largely imagined attentions of the Western press. She often felt that Kim enjoyed the intrigue for its own sake; and in the past few months he had even taken to sending her messages and telegrams in childish code, which she'd had to destroy at once, for fear of Lennie spotting them; or of telephoning late at night, often the worse for drink, and murmuring muddled endearments down the line, knowing that he must have been imperiling their relationship. And when, at their next clandestine meeting, she protested, he would either fob off the incident as a joke or become profusely contrite, then march her into the Intourist Beriozka and carry away some extravagant gift—twelve dozen red roses, five hundred grams of Beluga, a pair of mink ear muffs—all charged to his personal account, which was one of the many privileges he enjoyed over his adopted countrymen. And afterward, lying in bed in his book-lined flat—the address of which he'd made her swear to reveal to no one—they would listen to Beethoven's violin sonatas and play with his two Burmese kittens, Donald and Guy, who were fed a dash of Scotch every morning in their saucer of milk.

Then, over the past month, the shadow had begun to

fall. Kim's moods of depression, which were frequent but usually short-lived, now sometimes persisted for days on end; and his drinking, which had always been heavy but never offensive, started to get out of control. On several occasions he had been drunk when they met and had passed out before the end of the evening. Sometimes he had been too drunk even to leave his flat, let alone make love; and at times she had noticed a flash of suppressed rage which she found all the more worrying because there seemed no reason for it.

One evening a week ago she had been trying to coax him into the bedroom when he had suddenly lashed out with his fist, hitting the solid wooden door and spraining two fingers. But she had stubbornly consoled herself with the knowledge that her lover was an exceptional man, with exceptional problems. Even in their easiest moments together, Kim never discussed his professional life, and she had been wise enough not to ask. She just hoped, desperately, that it was his employers that were causing him distress, not her: for the thought of losing him made her feel sick.

After the accident with his hand, four days had passed without a word from him; then the day before yesterday the telegram arrived: WOLF ALONE PINING FOR MOUSE STOP HAVE APPLIED TOURNIQUET TO SNAKEBITE STOP EREVAN.

The signature was of the Erevan Restaurant in Moscow, which they used as a convenient rendezvous between her flat and his office in Dzerzhinski Square. When they'd met there that evening at 5:30, Kim had seemed a changed man: a little pale, perhaps, but his eyes had been clear, his hands steady, his mood at once serious and affectionate. He'd started by promising her that he was giving up "snakebite" for good, and made the point by drinking only tea; then, between little hugs and pecks, he'd put his plan to her for the weekend down in Gagra.

For such an enterprise it was surprisingly short notice. Kim usually planned these weekends, with characteristic precision, at least ten days in advance, giving her time to deceive Lennie with the pretext that she was making one of her regular visits to her brother in Copenhagen. Besides, there was now an added risk. For over the last couple of weeks she had begun to sense that Lennie's suspicions of her had been somehow confirmed. It was nothing she could put her finger on: just the odd snide remark, the surreptitious way he'd ask where she'd been, where she was going—but enough to make her extra wary.

At this last meeting in the Erevan, however, Kim had dismissed her fears with a pat on the arm and the assurance that she had no more cause to worry about Lennie. Then later, over dinner, he had made an oblique suggestion that she should pack up everything and move in with him; and there was even a hint, offered half-jokingly, that she might seek a divorce from that distant husband of hers, whom she'd last heard of running a hotel in Torquay.

When they parted, she had almost broken down and wept with joy. But his manner had remained quiet and businesslike, as he produced her air ticket to Sochi and her first-class train reservation on to Gagra. His instructions had been clear, and he'd repeated them twice: she was to check into the Grand Hotel and wait for him down in the lobby, not in their suite. He had promised to join her before evening.

She had waited till after eight o'clock.

The chandeliers were turned on, reflected a hundred times in galleries of ormolu mirrors. A bald man in striped pajamas appeared, shouted at an invisible waiter, then went out again. From the esplanade came the last wailings of private enterprise: crones in white shawls like headstones, hawking fruit and fish and ballpoint pens.

At 8:15 a party of men in brown suits and dark glasses filed through to the dining room. Natives, as well as visitors to Gagra, were too used to Western tourists to give more than a glance at the woman sitting alone on the satin couch in the corner.

By the norm of most Soviet women, Mrs. Joyce Warburton still looked young. She had good skin, under rather too much make-up, large features, and eyes the color of weak tea. Her clothes were unostentatious, with the hemline slightly longer than the Western fashion, so as to conceal her somewhat stout legs. At a cocktail party in the English Home Counties she might have been thought a trifle common; but alone in the forlorn elegance of a onetime Imperial palace on the Black Sea she had a certain chic.

Philby spotted her at once, and crossed over with a happy smile. "My little pet."

She stood up and clung to him, careless of the damage to her hair. "Oh, Kim! Kim!"

He gently unwrapped her arms and, still holding her around the waist, led her toward the dining room. "I'm famished. This air, Joyce—what a tonic after Moscow—I even walked from the station."

"But what kept you?" she cried. "I've been waiting since four. I was worried."

"My little mouse." He squeezed her tightly, guiding her to a table in the corner. "I got held up at the last minute. Duty to the workers' state."

"Oh, I'm so glad you're here," she said, as he evaded a further kiss by pulling out her chair.

The head waiter, hearing them speak English, offered

them a Union Jack on a little pedestal from a nearby table; but Kim waved it away. "No point in advertising," he said, laughing, and ordered fresh sturgeon, half a bottle of wine for Joyce, and mineral water for himself.

"You're being so strong-minded," she said.

"Just keeping a clear head," he said, smiling.

She squeezed his hand. "I'm so happy, Kim."

"So am I, Joyce. Happier than I've been for years."

They ate to the accompaniment of long speeches in Spanish, broken by noisy applause, from the delegation of brown-suited men at a table along the wall, laid with flags that Philby identified as representing the Democratic Republic of Cuba.

"Kim, let's go and live in Cuba!" she cried suddenly, then paused. His smile was a little slow in coming. "Cuba would be all right, wouldn't it? I mean, it's a Communist country, isn't it?"

"What makes you think I want to leave Moscow, Joyce?"

"Well—nothing." She looked down at her plate. Her face was slightly flushed and under the make-up he could see the lines on her neck. For a moment the conversation sagged like a fallen kite, but he quickly played out more line and had it fluttering up again. He was a master of small talk, able to make even the most ponderous conversation seem light and easy. It was a virtue that had paid off well in his life, and like all vain men he enjoyed practicing his talents even when they weren't required.

He was helped by a playful interlude during the main course, when a huge ginger cat strolled over to them and began rubbing itself against his leg. He was transported with delight, and even lifted the great creature onto the table and offered it a bite of his sturgeon. To his amusement the animal merely sniffed at the fish and struggled to be let down.

"Nothing for the RSPCA to complain about there!" he cried. "God, what a handsome beast."

He ordered her a second half-bottle of champagne, and a brandy and liqueur chocolates. She had a weak head, and was soon chattering about her schemes for making money out of Lennie's French employer. "It would be lovely to have a nice nest egg in the West," she murmured. "It could be transferred from a Swiss bank straight here—at least, to Moscow. We'd be rich, Kim."

He smiled and patted her hand. If he had grown up in another era than the Cambridge of the thirties, he thought wryly, he might have made a career out of silly rich women.

But poor Joyce Warburton—she didn't have a bean to her name; just a lot of random information that she'd no doubt picked up from that scavenger, Lennie Maddox, and which, if pieced together by a discriminating mind, could prove highly damaging, even disastrous. And in a dangerous moment Philby caught himself feeling almost sorry for her.

They stayed until the Cuban delegation had left, and a few locals were finishing their coffee. It was past eleven when he called for the bill. The waiter wanted to know if he would pay with Intourist coupons, but Philby settled in rubles, leaving a generous tip.

Joyce was all for going to bed, but he insisted on a walk by the sea. She agreed reluctantly, and with some surprise. He was an inveterately lazy man where physical exercise was concerned, always boasting of how he never walked when he could take a taxi.

The night was still warm and the water was as flat as a

mirror. They crossed the esplanade, down the stone steps to the short shelving beach where the tide sucked at the pebbles with a sound which he said reminded him of rustling petticoats. They reached a row of skiffs lying on their sides above the tidemark. "Joyce, let's take one."

"But there's no one to pay," she cried. "You can't just take one!"

"Nonsense. These boats belong to the People—and we're people, surely?"

"Very special people!" she giggled, as he tipped the narrow twin-oared skiff upright and began to slide it down toward the water. His sprained fingers no longer bothered him; and with a smile he remembered that he hadn't handled an oar since Trinity.

The old woman who came into the waiting room to open the bar thought at first the man was drunk. He was lying across one of the tables, breathing hard. As soon as she began rattling up the shutters, he woke and came over to her. *"Konyak,"* he whispered.

From his suit and tie she took him for another erring Muscovite. A middle-aged hooligan, she decided, as she poured a thimble measure of cheap Armenian brandy and held it back while the man counted out twelve kopeks. He swallowed it in a gulp, then returned to the table, where he was soon asleep again with his head on his arm. He woke twenty minutes later, with a bell clanging on the platform announcing the arrival of the express to Sochi. She watched him lope outside, and mouthed an elaborate Georgian oath as she glimpsed him climbing aboard the first-class sleeping car. These accursed Muscovites, coming down here with their pockets stuffed with rubles, getting drunk and chasing the girls, then riding home in the lap of luxury, while decent folk had to get up before dawn so that these parasites could play.

She was still muttering to herself when the train pulled out. Kim Philby had climbed into the upper berth, too tired even to undress. Except when he was awakened to show his ticket, he slept the six hours to Rostov-on-Don.

# 1 2 3 4 5 6 7 8 ⑨
# 10 11 12 13 14 15 16

*Cayle woke in a plain wooden room. Beside his* head the joins in the planking oozed a syrupy pine sap. There was a single naked bulb hanging from the ceiling, a shuttered window, and a stove like an igloo built of boiled sweets that roared softly in the corner.

He was alone, lying on a bed with a bright woolen blanket over him and a bolster under his head. He was fully dressed except for his boots; and the tops of his socks and the back of his trousers were damp. His mouth felt as though he were wearing a mask, and when he moved his lips he could feel dried blood flaking off his chin. He tried to sit up and a pain jarred through his neck, making him want to vomit. He lay back, swallowing bile and trying to steady the lurching patterns under his eyelids.

He didn't hear the door open, and had no idea how long the man had been standing there. He stood close to the bed and said, "Feeling better?"

"Ah, shit." Cayle made another effort to sit up, and subsided again with the pain. "Where the hell—where is this?"

"Lie still," the man said. His face was a pale blur. He turned and left the room, closing the door without a sound.

He'd spoken English, thought Cayle, with no accent. Like the men in the car. In the heart of Mother Russia. And without moving his head, he looked at his watch— 3:17. He tried remembering how long they'd been on the train—one, one and a half hours?—leaving Moscow at eleven. Over four hours ago.

He touched his jacket pocket and felt his wallet in place; he put his hand in and found his passport was there, too. If it wasn't for his bloody neck—

This time he heard the door open, and a second man came in. He was wearing a belted leather coat and he stood for what seemed a long time looking down at Cayle with the dispassion of a doctor doing his rounds. Cayle looked back at him with a swollen smile. "Hello, Sergeant. Bit far from your manor, isn't it?"

Dempster pulled up a chair and sat astride it with his arms resting along the straight wooden back. He lowered his chin onto his hands so that his shoulders were level with his ears, and said, "Feel up to answering some questions?"

"You've got a bloody nerve!" Cayle gave up grinning; it was too painful. "Suppose I ask *you* some questions?"

"Such as?"

"Such as why a couple of hoodlums from the Special Branch are running loose behind the Curtain, indulging in assault and kidnapping against friendly nationals. I mean, it wouldn't look good if it ever got out."

"It won't get out," said Dempster quietly. "I owe you an apology," he added, after a pause. "There's been a balls-up."

"Oh, that's rich, Sergeant! You mean, you and your mate were planning to snatch the fat Frenchman, and got me instead?" He was trying to think quickly. It was Philby who had arranged his ticket, he remembered: and had presumably arranged the tickets for Pol and Galina Valisova. And had Cayle's ticket been bought in Philby's name? The implications were too vast; they became scrambled in his brain and exploded with a slamming headache. He gripped the sides of the bed and gulped with nausea. "Keep going, mate, and they might even give you a job tracing parking tickets."

"Don't start getting cheeky again, Cayle. Not out here; we're too far behind the lines."

"Too far for what? Knocking me off and burying me somewhere peaceful under the pine trees?"

For a long half-minute Dempster just sat and stared at him. "You were almost right, Cayle," he said at last. "We didn't want you. We wanted Philby. According to our sources, he was booked on the same train, same compartment."

"I'd change sources."

"Working out here isn't easy," Dempster said patiently. "We budget for a certain margin of wastage. Such as you."

"Thanks. What do you want?"

"Everything you know—beginning with those few points we wanted cleared up in London, before you bolted. A mistake, that—on our part. I should have asked you to surrender your passport."

"And if I hadn't?"

Dempster shrugged. "You're familiar with Section Six of the Official Secrets Act? Conspiracy to commit an offense under the act. I could have got you for covering up about your meeting with Jameson-Clarke."

"You may think so. But not the big boys. Not the men with the quiet ties who run your Majesty's bloody Britannic government while warming their arses round the old club fire. They're not stupid, Dempster. *They'd* never have sent you out here to start playing rough. I wonder who did?"

There was another pause, while Dempster just looked at him. Finally he said: "Let me tell you something, Cayle. Just because you've walked into what looks to you like an important story, don't make the mistake of thinking you're

( 161

important. You're not. You're dispensable, chum. Remember that." He sunk his chin still lower and began sucking the knuckle of his broad flat thumb. "Let's start again with that lunch at the Ritz."

For almost an hour, although it seemed much longer, Cayle talked. He told everything from the beginning, and Dempster listened without moving, almost without speaking, except to elucidate some small detail. He took no notes, made no threats. But if he believed Cayle, and was satisfied, he showed no sign of it. He showed no sign of anything—no surprise, no curiosity—and at the end of it, all he said was, "Would you like a glass of water?"

"I'd like to get the hell out," said Cayle.

Dempster nodded and stood up. "Well, I don't think there's any reason to detain you."

"Except that I'm out here in the flaming boondocks! I haven't even got my bloody anorak, or my boots."

"You've got your passport and money," Dempster said, turning to the door. "You'll make it." He went out and the door closed.

Like hell I'll make it, thought Cayle. He lay back and stared at the naked bulb. For the first time he realized how warm it was in the room; his neck and armpits were damp with sweat. He began to regret that he hadn't taken Dempster up on his offer of a glass of water.

It was very quiet, except for the stove. He kicked off the blanket and carefully stood up. His body seemed very heavy, and he felt slightly drunk. He walked across the room in his stockinged feet and tried the door. It opened. Beyond was a pinewood passage with a door on either side, and at the end a third, larger door with black iron hinges and a Yale-type lock.

He moved softly on the balls of his feet until he was level with the two side doors, and listened. Nothing. He tried the one on the left, but it was locked; so was the door on the right, except that it had a lock with a sliding catch. He put his thumb under it and pressed, very gently. It slid back with a well-oiled click. The only light came from the room he'd just left, and what he could see ahead looked like a passage leading into darkness. The walls seemed to be made of some coarse rendering, with no doors. He came to a corner, turned, and started down another length of empty corridor. His hands were trembling; he took a slow, deep breath. At the end was a pair of steel doors with folding bars clamped across them, like an emergency exit in a cinema. He grabbed both bars and leaned his whole weight against them. There was a clang and a rush of icy air that left him breathless.

The door had plowed back at least six inches of fresh snow. Beyond was a broad street with dark windows opposite rising eight floors high. It was still dark, except for pricks of street-lighting stretching at long intervals into the distance. The wide troughs from the snowplows had been covered with a recent fall, and along the snow-packed pavements was the occasional hump of a half-buried car.

He looked at the nearest car, and thought: Find if it's unlocked, open the hood, cross the wires. He'd learned the trick as a kid back at Blue Water. It was a cinch, even in ninety degrees in the shade—all you had to worry about was the sweat getting in your eyes.

His face was numb, his feet were like great sacks dragging through the snow. He reached some steps and a heavy door, locked, with no bell. Opposite were two cars. He stumbled sideways and leaned against the first one, his naked hand fumbling under the snow for the door handle.

He found it, but it didn't move. He tried the next car, and sank onto his knees. The snow had a thick feathery feeling; it wasn't wet or even cold. He reached up and his fingers tightened around a bar of burning metal. He heard a humming sound growing into the steady beat of snow tires. Then a hush: the mutter of an engine, a door slamming, the shuffle of boots and steaming white breath. A hand shaking his shoulder, another pulling him to his feet. He was held by leather gloves and there were faces framed in ear flaps, and voices, quiet and unhurried, as his feet left the ground and his back and buttocks bumped against something hard. Doors slammed again, it was warm, and the ground began to move.

He put his hands down to steady himself and felt nothing. A draft of hot air touched him, lulled him, his head sliding sideways and resting on metal. The metal drummed against his head with a painless rhythm. There was a jolt, a shout, a crash of doors, and he was half dragged, half carried, down steps and across a strip of concrete, through swing-doors into an aching light. His legs were stretched out, his socks peeled off his bloodless feet. A woman in a white coat felt his wrist; someone else loosened his belt, pulled down his trousers, wrapped his legs in a blanket, and he was lifted onto a trolley covered with a rubber sheet. He felt a sharp ache above the elbow, and saw the woman in the white coat pressing down the plunger of the hypodermic, as his mouth filled with a thick bittersweet taste.

Drugs, he thought: the new science of torture. He yelled and yanked his arm free, feeling the needle snap off in the muscle. The woman spoke angrily, and hands grabbed his shoulders and forced his head back onto the rubber sheet.

A man's voice began speaking his name, spelling the letters out in Russian, as the needle went in again and he listened to the words, "Passport," "Aeroflot, "Londra," fading as the trolley began to move and a warm fuzziness crept up from his toes. He was walking on the ceiling, trying to step over the strip-lighting and the green-painted girders. But the effort was too much; his head lolled sideways and rolled away into emptiness.

He heard a short scream, a splash, a series of thumps, then silence.

He was lying in a narrow white-tiled cell with a spy hole in the green metal door. They had removed his underpants, and he lay naked between the clammy rubber and a rough linen sheet frayed with laundering. It was an iron bed high off the ground and had pairs of leather straps hanging loose on either side. On the floor were duckboards over a sluice hole, and the air was warm and stale with disinfectant.

He got up cautiously, testing his fingers and toes. They had a dull disconnected feeling. He balanced himself against the bed and managed the three steps to the door. There was no handle. He shouted, "Hello!" and was answered by howls and groans, as he began to beat his fists against the door. There was a rapid padding of feet outside, and the door swung inward, knocking him back against the bed.

A short square man in a white cap and smock, like a butcher, looked at him for a moment, then stepped forward and pulled the door shut with a slam. From somewhere close came a thin ululating wail, followed by a snatch of song.

A couple of minutes later the door opened again. The

orderly in the smock stood aside, and a tall man wearing a suit and tie came in. He paused to put on a pair of wire-rimmed spectacles, then said in English: "What is it you want, please?"

"I want to know where the hell I am!"

"This is a night station for alcoholics," the man replied.

"I'm not a bloody alcoholic!" Cayle roared.

The man studied him through his spectacles and said, "It is necessary to explain why you were in the street without shoes or sufficient clothes, at four o'clock in the morning, in a temperature of more than thirteen degrees below zero. You are fortunate you did not lose certain of your extremities."

"I wasn't drunk," said Cayle.

The man gave a slight shrug. "You will wait here until your case is investigated."

"I want to talk to the police now. I have something urgent to tell them." But as he spoke, the orderly pushed him back against the bed.

"Your case will be investigated," the tall man repeated, and they both went out and the door slammed shut again.

The commissionaire stepped in front of him and said, "Can I help you?" Cayle noted that the "sir" was offensively lacking.

"I want to see Mr. Simon Hann—Chancery."

"Got an appointment?"

"No. Just tell him it's Cayle—C for crap, A for arse . . ."

"Wait here." The commissionaire went back into his cubicle and lifted a telephone. At the same moment a grey-haired man appeared from a side door and paused, looking at Cayle.

"Are you waiting for someone?"

"I've got a lunch date with the Ambassador's wife," said Cayle.

The man was still thinking of the right thing to say when the commissionaire returned.

"Mr. Hann is engaged at present," he said, with pedantic satisfaction. "But if you'll fill in this form, I'll find out if someone else can see you."

"It's got to be Hann or nobody," said Cayle. "Tell him · it's a matter of international importance."

"Excuse me." The grey-haired man had moved closer. "Are you a British subject, sir?"

Cayle turned his bruised, unshaven face toward him and leered, "No, and I've forgotten my black tie, too. Now will you stop pretending this is White's, and get me Mr. Hann, and smartish!"

The man turned stiffly to the commissionaire. "Give the gentleman the form, Albert. Will you wait here, please," he added to Cayle, and strutted back through the side door.

Cayle took the sheet of paper with the Embassy heading, and against the question NATURE OF BUSINESS wrote "confidential," then handed it back to the commissionaire, who grudgingly returned with it to his cubicle. Cayle sat down on a mock Empire sofa and waited.

Hann came down ten minutes later. He looked sleek and calm. "Hello, Mr. Cayle. I heard you'd gone to Leningrad with the rest of your people."

"I had. That's what I want to talk to you about."

Hann glanced at his watch. "I can spare you only a few minutes. I've an appointment at eleven." He turned and led Cayle briskly toward the elevator.

His office was a small impersonal room on the second floor. Cayle hung up his new muskrat coat, which he'd bought on his way here from GUM, along with a new pair of boots and gloves, and sat down under Annigoni's portrait of the Queen, while Hann walked around behind a leather-topped desk.

"You look terrible, Cayle. Have you been drinking?"

"No. But I could do with one."

Hann ignored him. "You said it was important. What's happened?"

"I got beaten up and spent most of the night in a sobering-up station. They gave me several injections against frostbite and fined me fifty rubles."

"And I suppose you got robbed, too? Well, if they've taken your passport, you'll have to go to your own Embassy. We can't help—even if you are a British resident."

"Thanks," said Cayle, "but as it happens, they didn't take my passport, or anything else. Just me. I was grabbed off the Red Arrow Express to Leningrad last night. They knocked me cold in the toilet, and I woke up in some building back here in Moscow. I managed to get away, but without my coat or boots, and damned near froze to death before the cops found me."

Hann had picked up a feather-stemmed ballpoint and began stroking it against his cheek. "Have you reported this to the police?"

"No."

"Why not?"

"I wanted to, but then after they let me out of the medical station, I reasoned I'd had enough trouble without trying to explain everything to the Moscow cops. For a start, they probably wouldn't believe me. Even if they did believe me, it would be months before they let me go."

"They'd be able to check easily enough if the train had been stopped and any of the passengers were missing," said Hann. "Or is there something more to all this?"

Cayle paused. "Have you got that drink?"

"It'll have to be a quick one." He opened a drawer in the desk and took out a glass and a bottle of Dimple Haig. He didn't look like a secret drinker, thought Cayle, but then, they never did.

"Do you mind having it straight?" said Hann.

"Fine." Cayle got up and swallowed half of it standing. He returned to his chair and said: "Ever heard of a chap called Mayhew? MI5 liaison man with the Home Office."

Hann placed the feather pen back in its holder. "What about him?"

"He called on me just before I left London. Wanted to ask some questions about Sir Roger Jameson-Clarke. There was a Special Branch man with him called Dempster—Sergeant Dempster."

Hann sat watching him with his cold oily stare. "And what has all this got to do with last night?"

"Just that Sergeant Dempster was one of the boys who grabbed me off the Red Arrow Express. Afterward he got me talking for about an hour, and I told him everything. Then, when he'd left me, I just walked out, too. I guess it was what I was supposed to do—walk into the snow and do a Captain Oates."

"What exactly did you tell him?"

"As I said, everything. All about Comrade Kim, and my meeting with him, and my meetings with Maddox, and my conversation with you." He drank some whisky. "All right, I wasn't trying for any medal. Dempster had slugged me pretty efficiently, and I didn't get the impression he was fooling around."

"Just a moment," Hann said. He lifted the phone and asked someone to cancel his eleven o'clock appointment. "Now let's try to get some of this straight. You were traveling last night on the Red Arrow Express to Leningrad when someone stopped the train and attacked you in the lavatory?"

"I told you—it was Dempster. There were two of them, and they attacked me as I opened the door, without making sure I was the right person."

"Are you trying to say they were after someone else?"

"That's right. Dempster must have checked my empty bunk when he came aboard, after somehow finding out who'd made the booking. And it wasn't me."

"Who?"

"Kim Philby."

For a moment Hann's guard dropped: there was a tight crease at the corner of his mouth and his eyes seemed to have gone dead; they were not looking at Cayle or at anything else. And suddenly Cayle knew. It was with a flash of understanding in which everything became clear: even the wildest events of the last few days now seemed so obvious and simple: the whole elaborate squalid racket from the beginning, more than twelve years ago, right up to the final unplayed act.

Hann recovered quickly. He opened the drawer and brought out the whisky bottle again, with a second glass. "You'd better have another yourself," he said. "This may take some time."

All Cayle's good sense now warned him to get clear before it was too late; but his professional instincts were more powerful. Millions of printed words had been spent on the Philby story—books, articles, theories, explanations, assertions, assumptions, deductions—while all the time the truth had been lying just below the surface, known to only a tiny cabal of conspirators, traitors, and spy catchers.

It was a messy, vicious truth. But Barry Cayle had grown up with a simple faith in truth as an unqualified virtue. He might cheat on his expenses, but he would not cheat on a story; and while others in his predicament might have sought escape in expediency and humbug, Cayle stood by the duties of his trade; for in his rougher, humbler calling he was like an archeologist who stumbles on the vital clue that invalidates a whole tradition of knowledge and accepted fact.

He was also, with a certain clumsy innocence, a brave man; for he knew now that he was walking a very narrow line. With Hann, the perils might not be as immediate as they had been with Dempster. The difference was that with Dempster, Cayle had still been ignorant, and could thus afford to be honest. Once in possession of the truth, he also became part of the conspiracy; from now on he would have to live the lie like the rest of them—by bluff, guile, and subterfuge. And for the first time he began to experience perhaps something of what Kim Philby had had to live with for more than thirty years.

This first ordeal, with Hann, continued for just over two hours, with an interruption for sandwiches and coffee. Hann's approach was less direct than Dempster's, but nonetheless dangerous for that. He was quick, treacherous, and sly. His one lapse, when the mask had slipped for those few vital seconds, was not repeated. For the rest of the session, he remained in perfect control.

Like Dempster, he wanted to know everything that Cayle knew; and Cayle not only had to supply him with the satisfactory answers, but also to imply by those answers that he believed Hann to be something that he was not. Cayle decided from the start that his best role would be his most natural one: tough, rough, honest, and gullible.

When he had finished, Hann smiled suavely and said, "The only thing that puzzles me, Cayle, is why you chose to come to me?"

"Because you tried to warn me off," said Cayle. "It's always a mistake with newspapers, and newspapermen. Your boys tried the same thing with us when we first broke the Philby story. You leaned too hard. Newspapers are funny that way—they tend to get bloody-minded if they think the authorities are holding out on them."

"You're going to have a job writing this story," said Hann. "As far as this fellow Dempster's concerned, you've no proof, no witnesses, nothing to back you up except a file in a Moscow sobering-up station and a receipt for a fifty-ruble fine. Hardly effective evidence."

"You believe it," said Cayle.

Hann took a cigarette out of a black leather case and sat examining the end without lighting it. "I'm not saying whether I believe it or not. My job is to collect information—not to evaluate it."

Cayle finished his drink and stood up. "Oh, I know, Hann, you're in the clear—you're just the errand boy. You don't have to worry about your own skin—just the reputations of a moldering old gang of starch-shirted mandarins who fell for the great Marxist daydream of the thirties and didn't have the guts to come clean while the damage was being done. Because remember, those bastards aren't just accomplices to treason, before and after the fact. They've also got blood on their hands. Philby had a lot of men killed, one way and another, and the old boys you're supposed to be protecting allowed him to get away with it."

"I think I've heard enough," Hann said quietly; he sat with his cigarette burning away between his fingers, the ash beginning to curl like a grey claw. "I shall be making a full report on what you've told me, and will pass it on to the appropriate authorities. Meanwhile, I suggest you contact your own Embassy and make arrangements to return home before you get yourself into any more trouble." He stood up and came around the desk. "By the way, your friend Leonard Maddox was killed last night."

"Killed?"

"He was run over by a truck behind the Bolshoi."

"Hit and run?"

"As a matter of fact, it was," said Hann. "How did you know?"

"I heard some people talking about it in the hotel."

"Yes, nasty business. He lived with an Englishwoman here, and we're having some difficulty tracing her. But again, not much of a story."

"I'm not thinking of writing anything yet. The big story hasn't begun."

"Good afternoon, Mr. Cayle." Hann waited until the door closed, then reached for his glass and found it was empty. He poured himself another, looked at the telephone, hesitated, then downed his whisky in a gulp.

Downstairs the commissionaire checked Cayle's departure at 1:12 P.M. in the Embassy log.

At 1:25 the taxi dropped him outside the Hotel Rossija, on the south side of Red Square. He had chosen this hotel because it was the largest and most anonymous of all the hotels in Moscow: four gargantuan slabs of plate-glass and concrete forming an unlovely rectangle the size of the Kremlin, with accommodation for 15,000 guests. It was an excellent place in which to get lost and stay lost.

He went through the obligatory routine of handing in his coat to the cloakroom attendant, then joining one of the many queues for the travel desk. Half an hour later he faced a girl who looked like an out-of-work ballerina: sharp cheekbones, long neck, too much eye shadow. He handed her his passport and asked her to make him a reservation on the next flight to Leningrad. She opened his passport at the three-day visa, made a quick note on a pad beside her, and said: "If you would wait over there, sir, please." She nodded at a row of leather chairs, all of them occupied. "You will be informed in fifteen minutes if there is a reservation."

Cayle thanked her, without getting a response, and sauntered away in search of the sauna and barbershop. Both were full, with long queues outside; and in the downstairs restaurant every table was taken. The three bars were crowded to the doors. He wandered finally into the Beriozka, where rows of American and Scandinavian tourists were poring over trays of amber, painted wooden dolls, mink and muskrat, and machine-made peasant blouses. The only caviar was the red brand that came in tubes, like shaving cream.

Twenty minutes later he was back at the travel desk, going straight to the head of the queue. The girl looked up at him, gave a sideways nod, and two men stepped forward. They stood very close to him, one on either side, without actually touching him.

"Mr. Kay-eel? You will come." He was a couple of inches shorter than Cayle, with a round pale face pitted and spongy like fresh bread, and black hair combed flat across his scalp. His companion was taller, broader, with a slack mouth and colorless eyes. Both wore suits of grey artificial fiber that were too tight at the shoulders and too loose around the legs.

The small one nodded in the direction of the main

entrance, and the three of them began to move in a close trio across the crowded floor. Near the doors Cayle said, "I've got a coat—a new one."

Both men ignored him. A group of tourists came in, laughing and unslinging cameras. None of them glanced at Cayle or his escort. He began to feel rather lonely and unimportant.

Outside, there was an icy mist and the crust of the snow was turning soggy. A grey truck was double-parked next to the taxi rank. A man in a fur-lined military cap and bulky blue overcoat sat at the wheel. A second uniformed man sat in the back, with a short-muzzled machine-pistol slung across his waist. Cayle sat in front, between the driver and the smaller of the two plain-clothes men. The other got in the back, and without a word they started off.

There were no sirens, no militiamen halting the traffic. They passed the long queue outside the Lenin Mausoleum and stopped for the lights at the corner of the GUM store. Cayle didn't bother to ask where they were going. They crossed into Svedlova Square, between the Bolshoi and the Metropol, and started up Karl Marx Prospekt, keeping with the traffic in the outside lane. The mist seemed to be getting heavier; most of the traffic was now driving on side lights, and around the edge of Dzerzhinski Square there were lights in many of the windows. They turned left into Dzerzhinski Street, then hard right, under a concrete arch, and pulled up in front of a red-and-white pole.

Two sentries with automatic rifles stepped forward and peered in on either side, their breath thickening the mist. The driver flashed his headlights twice, and the red-and-white pole swung up. The truck moved forward, into a tall grey courtyard where the snow had been stamped down into boot patterns of dirty ice. The driver kept in bottom gear, around the edge of the yard, until they reached a low doorway. The small plain-clothes man next to Cayle opened the truck door and stepped down. Cayle followed, gasping with the cold.

Inside the building a flight of concrete stairs ended at a padded door. The small man pushed it open and there was a rush of warm air. The corridor beyond was painted the color of milk chocolate. The only sound was a low humming like the inside of a great ship. The plain-clothes man stopped at an unmarked door and opened it without knocking, then motioned Cayle inside.

It was a narrow office with a steel filing cabinet, a desk, a bench, and a tube of fluorescent lighting that fizzed and flickered from the ceiling. A woman with straight grey hair and rimless glasses sat at the desk under a faded brown photograph of Lenin and peered at Cayle over the top of an antique typewriter. The plain-clothes man nodded Cayle toward the bench, closed the door, and stood with his back to it. He spoke rapidly to the woman, who inserted a double sheet of pink duplicating paper into the typewriter; then said to Cayle: "To empty your pockets, please!"

Cayle was beginning to feel like a schoolboy caught out in a misdemeanor. The plain-clothes man took each item and described it in Russian, and the woman punched out the words with two fingers on the typewriter, while the man arranged the miscellaneous belongings on the desk beside her: keys to Thackeray Mansions and the Moke, wallet, passport, traveler's checks, dollars and rubles in cash, press cards and letters of introduction, and Lennie Maddox's business card. Also a sheaf of used air tickets from London to Moscow via Kabul, with a wad of receipts to correspond—all to keep the accounts people happy back in London, and as good as a written confession of his devious itinerary back into the Soviet Union. Finally, there was his ticket and reservation on the Red Arrow Express to Leningrad, dated the night before.

The whole procedure took forty minutes and filled two double pages of pink paper. The plain-clothes man laid them out on the desk, produced a pen and jabbed it at Cayle. "Please, to sign!" Cayle signed; and the plain-clothes man gathered the pages up and stuffed them into his inside pocket. "Please, to follow." Cayle followed, down more milk-chocolate corridor, and stopped at another unmarked door. The plain-clothes man opened it and stood aside. "Please, to wait."

Cayle glanced inside and said, "How long do I wait?" It was the first question he'd asked since leaving the Hotel Rossija.

"To wait here," the man repeated; he stepped back and closed the door, and Cayle heard the sound of a key.

It was an odd room. There was a tiled floor, a small window with frosted pebble glass but no bars, a camp bed with a grey blanket, a table and two chairs, a plain overhead light, and a half-portion leading to a basin with one tap and a lavatory without a seat. It was spartan and military: not so much a cell as the sort of room a commanding officer might use on maneuvers or at the front. It was clean and there was no smell.

Cayle tried the tap on the basin. The water was icy. He took off his jacket and shirt, and sluiced down his face and the back of his neck and dried himself on a corner of the blanket. Then he looked at his watch—the only thing they'd left him besides his clothes. It was 3:45. He felt dirty, unshaven, and dog-tired.

He turned out the light, dragged off his shoes and trousers, and lay down under the blanket and dropped into a dreamless sleep.

He was awakened by someone shaking his shoulder. He blinked up at the light and saw a tall man standing by the bed. He wore a dark-blue suit, white shirt, dark tie; his mouth was straight and without expression. He said: "It is time for you to wake up, Mr. Cayle." His English was relaxed and almost without accent.

Cayle said stupidly, "What time is it?"—then looked at his watch. It was a few minutes before six. "I'll be with you in a moment," he added. He went behind the partition and shook his head under the cold tap.

The Russian said, "I'm sorry we don't have a towel to offer you. This room is not often used." He waited until Cayle was ready, then opened the door and let him go out first, switching the light off after them.

"Is it far?" said Cayle.

"No, not far," the Russian said. He walked briskly, with the movements of a man who kept himself fit. They came to another padded door, which led into a wider, higher corridor with dark paneling and a green-and-white-checkered marble floor. Cayle guessed that they had entered the older half of the building—the one that had been the offices of an insurance company in Czarist days, before it became part of the Lubyanka Prison and administration headquarters of the Committee of State Security.

They reached a tall porticoed door. The Russian tapped gently and turned the brass knob. Holding the door half-open, Cayle heard him say, "He's here, sir," in his controlled meticulous English.

Cayle did not catch the reply. The Russian opened the door farther and Cayle went in.

It was a large room with curtains half-drawn across a window overlooking the square. There was a lot of highly polished buhl furniture, including a heavy ornamental desk and a black marble lamp with a red-and-gold tasseled shade. Behind the desk, in a wing chair upholstered in green velvet, a man sat with his head half turned to the window, and the lamp cast a pink glow across his profile, with its thin prominent nose and wing of silver hair. He turned enough to give Cayle a faint, apologetic smile. "Come in—do sit down."

Cayle was used to surprises in his job. He only wished he were more presentable: being unshaven and still half asleep was no fit state in which to meet a man who until a few days ago had been a senior member of the British Foreign Service. Sir Roger Jameson-Clarke looked a little tired, a little pale, but otherwise he displayed the same patrician poise that he had shown in the Ritz and the Squadron.

"Now, Cayle. Perhaps you'd like to tell us what you've been up to in the last few days?"

1   2   3   4   5   6   7   8   9

(10)  11  12  13  14  15  16

*"The city is situated on more than two hundred* islands," the girl said. "Each island is linked by a bridge. There are altogether six hundred and one bridges." She spoke with the enthusiasm of an air hostess telling her passengers to fasten their seat belts.

"The city was constructed on a great marsh and its first foundations stood on wooden piles driven into the mud. These foundations also contain the bones of half a million slave laborers." The driver swung the wheel, and she put up her hand to shade her eyes against the arctic glare that reached in below the smoked upper panes of the coach windows. "On our left we now see, in the middle of the river, the Fortress of St. Peter and St. Paul." The driver changed gear with a noisy lurch and several of the passengers woke up. The girl steadied herself against the engine block and said, "The Fortress was used as a prison for many famous people. The most famous was Lenin."

"Which famous prisoners are in there now?" asked a man in a yellow gabardine suit near the back.

"Today it is used as a museum," the girl replied. "Now, to our right we see the Hermitage—"

The man in the gabardine suit put back his head and yawned. "Is this why they made us bolt our lunch? What do they think we are—a goddam Rotary outing from Burlington, Illinois?"

( 181

"Perhaps they have problems at the airport," said his companion, a lean young Frenchman with wiry black hair and a lot of complicated camera equipment piled beside him in the aisle.

"You boys expecting to get anything out of this?" asked the man in the gabardine suit; he had the flat ambiguous accent of an American who has lived a long time out of America.

"There could be a crash," said the Frenchman.

"There are no plane crashes in Russia, Yves. Everybody knows that."

"The plane is French," said Yves, smiling. "And French planes are surely allowed to crash?"

"You're a cynic," said the American. "You'd love that plane to crash."

"Normally, perhaps. But please, not when I am on it!"

They drove past an old man taking his dog for a walk. The dog was small and fat, like the man, and wore a leather coat strapped around his belly, and fur ear muffs. A couple of photographers in the coach took pictures of it. They were now crossing the frozen Neva and the girl was point-ing out the golden needle of the Admiralty spire. Near the far bank a hole had been cut in the ice and a group of men in bathing trunks and rubber caps were lowering them-selves in, watched by a small crowd. Several journalists in the coach laughed. "Some way to work off a hangover!" one of them shouted. The girl broke off and said, "They are champion swimmers of the Leningrad Sports Federa-tion. They practice like that all the year."

"I must say, she's a good-looker," said the American. "And I guess she makes out all right, too! That hat looks like mink."

"They say these Intourist guides all have lovers in the

Ministries or the KGB," said Yves. "I don't think they are available, except under special circumstances."

The American snickered. "You got a one-track mind, Yves. Sex and disaster." He leaned out and called to the girl: "When do we go to the airport?"

She frowned. "You want to go to the airport already?"

"Well, that's what we're all here for!" he cried.

The girl spoke quickly with the driver, who swung the wheel, throwing the girl completely off balance this time, so that she slipped sideways and fell against the door. Her apple cheeks flushed darkly, and she clutched at her white fur hat, righted herself, and smoothed down her black coat. "If it is your wish," she said, with dignity, "we will go to the airport."

They drove back across the river and rejoined the shabby elegance of the Nevsky Prospekt, running wide and straight into the horizon. The girl sat down beside the driver and most of the journalists dozed.

They entered the airport at a far corner, away from the international passenger terminal. The gate was manned by grey-uniformed Frontier Police, who came aboard and checked their special passes issued by the Press Office of the Foreign Ministry.

"Please, from here there must be no photographs," the girl said as the guards stepped down and the bus began to move forward again, down a muddy avenue into a sprawling complex of cinder-block huts.

The afternoon sky was icy blue, with no wind, and across the Gulf of Finland lay the faint smudge of Kronstadt Island.

The VIP lounge in the international terminal was packed and noisy. At around three o'clock fleets of official cars began drawing up outside; and at 3:20 there was a flutter of interest as the Troika-Caravelle prototype crept into view, escorted by uniformed outriders who snarled in and out under the wings and around the stout silver fuselage.

There were a few late arrivals from the press, who had evaded the official bus tour from the Europeiiski Hotel and made their way in their own cars or by taxi. One of them, a plump raddled-faced man in a greasy muskrat hat, had come sensibly equipped with a hip flask.

At 3:30 there was more mild excitement as a short, very fat bearded man in a vicuña coat stepped forward and introduced himself to the cameras as M. Charles Pol, the French entrepreneur responsible for the Troika-Caravelle deal; and at 3:45 the loudspeaker began to crackle out boarding instructions in Russian, French, and English. The embarkation was a wearisome affair, with two Frontier Police scrutinizing all passes once again. The only formality that had been dispensed with was the searching of hand luggage, which in this case consisted entirely of camera equipment, belonging mostly to the French contingent.

Charles Pol was the last to board the plane, waddling across the tarmac and up the embarkation steps, with the little Russian girl in the white mink hat trotting at his side, carrying his briefcase. He lowered himself into a reserved seat at the back of the plane, while the girl walked slowly up the aisle, glancing along each of the rows of triple seats. She passed the raddled-faced journalist with the hip flask, who was now taking a long drink. He looked as though he needed it: his hands shook and his eyes were watering from the cold. She gave him a quick smile, and he lowered the flask and nodded. Beside him, the American in the yellow gabardine suit said, "Miss, when do we get the champagne?"

"Refreshments will be served when we are in the air," she replied, and walked on, no longer looking along the seats, until she reached the head of the plane, where she switched on the cabin intercom. *"Gospoda!"* she announced, *"Mesdames et messieurs.* Ladies and gentlemen." She translated into the three languages: "Welcome aboard this inaugural flight of Troika-Caravelle One One Two, an aircraft which testifies to the combined skill and friendship existing between the French Republic and the Union of the Soviet Socialist Republics. Our pilots are Captain O. D. Prokovsky and Capitaine J. P. Duhamel—" She then began reading from the handout, translating each paragraph into the three languages, in the same passionless voice that she'd used on the coach.

The plane was a long-range twin-jet, with a high payload against a low fuel consumption and a short landing capability, making it ideal for internal Soviet air routes. It was also highly maneuverable at low altitudes, which recommended it as a radar-hopping military transport—though this secondary advantage was not mentioned in the handout, or by the girl. She concluded by announcing that the flight would last fifty minutes, heading due west over the Gulf of Finland, then south over the city of Tallinn and back along the coast of Estonia to Leningrad.

The fact that the aircraft bore no markings or national emblem aroused no particular interest. Indeed, most of the journalists had written their copy before leaving the hotel.

Five minutes after take-off, with Kronstadt rising like a grey bubble out of the flat mist of water seven miles below, a couple of Russian air hostesses came down the aisle with trays of *pâté de foie gras* sandwiches and glasses of French champagne. In an aisle seat halfway down, the raddled-faced journalist had taken out his hip flask again and poured its contents into his glass. The American in the gabardine suit smiled approvingly. "That's something every working journalist in Russia should carry, like a soldier carries a gun. What is it? Brandy?"

The man nodded and offered him the flask.

"Just a sniff," said the American. "Brandy and champagne give me heartburn. I'm more of a whisky man myself. Name's Roskoe," he added, "Ken Roskoe. Atlantic Syndicated News. I don't think we've met?"

"Fielding," said the man, putting away the flask.

"You're British?"

The man hesitated, as though with a slight impediment of speech. "Yes, that's right."

"Which paper?"

"The *Observer*."

"The London *Observer?*"

Fielding nodded and sipped his champagne cocktail.

"Doesn't the *Observer* have another man out here?" said Roskoe. "I've run into him a couple of times. Kind of studious type—speaks very good Russian."

"I'm free-lancing," Fielding said carefully. "For a supplement on air travel." The loudspeaker broke in with the Russian girl's voice telling them that they were now approaching the narrowest point of the Gulf of Finland, where the coast could be seen on both sides. They were flying at an altitude of 12,000 meters, at an air speed of 800 kilometers an hour.

"I just wish they'd cut that crap!" Roskoe muttered. "Show us a film or let us sleep—that's the way I like to travel." But Fielding seemed already to have taken him at his word: he had finished his drink, tilted his seat back, and closed his eyes. His *foie gras* sandwiches lay untouched on the tray in front of him.

At the back of the plane, across the aisle from the little Russian girl, Pol was beginning to sweat, despite the ample air-conditioning. Ten minutes later a tall blond man with a camera case slung over his shoulder got up and walked leisurely up the aisle, through the curtain leading to the forward cabin.

The Russian pilot was at the controls, leaning back against the headrest and watching the dark-blue horizon ahead. Beside him, the French co-pilot sat smoking and chatting to the interpreter in the jump seat behind. Both pilots had their earphones hanging loose around their necks. The interpreter was sitting adjacent to the Russian navigator, who was bending over a chart covered with a plastic overlay on which he was measuring distances with a pair of dividers. He made a note in the log beside him as the blond man slipped in and closed the communicating door.

He was a slim, pale man, and his corn-colored hair was tight and curly like a lambs-wool rug; his eyes were dead, and there was a clean white scar down one cheek that gave his face a stiff lopsided expression. He stepped up behind the Russian pilot and with an effortless movement drew a gun from his camera case and touched the barrel against the base of the man's cranium. He spoke in quiet pedantic French: "You will change course immediately and proceed north. Our destination is the Finnish coast— the peninsula of Björnvik, south of the town of Lovisa."

The communicating door opened again and shut quickly. One of the French photographers stood just behind the blond man, away from the crew. He had the body of a wrestler, and the gun in his hand had an unusually wide blunt barrel.

Capitaine Duhamel looked at them both and repeated the navigational instructions to Captain Prokovsky, speaking calmly in French through the interpreter. When he had finished, the blond man said: "No one is to move, except to carry out his duties. Do not attempt to make a mistake. I have a good knowledge of navigation and have studied this area with care."

The interpreter relayed the message without expression. He was a big middle-aged man in a shapeless suit. Captain Prokovsky leaned forward to move the controls, and even in the confined space the interpreter made a swift lunge, one broad hand with the fingers held rigid slicing down at the blond man's wrist. There was a loud thud above the hum of the engines, and the interpreter's head flopped back from his shoulders with a curious splashing sound; his knees struck the floor, he rolled over, slid down the back of Captain Prokovsky's seat, leaving a slimy red smear along the grey covering, thumped down at the navigator's feet and lay still.

The navigator gave a shout in Russian and came to his feet as the wide-barreled gun swung around and aimed at his belly. Both pilots had turned, and now recognized, in the French "photographer's" hand, the still experimental antipersonnel pistol for use against hijackers: the flat plastic bullet, with its lobbing trajectory, has a high velocity but a short range incapable of penetrating the skin of the fuselage, while having the same effect on the human body as the internationally proscribed dum-dum.

The blond man said: "Capitaine Duhamel, I am ordering you both again to change direction. If you have not done so within ten seconds, my colleague here will blow off your leg at the knee."

The French pilot's cigarette had gone out, and he sat motionless next to Captain Prokovsky. The blond man now turned to the navigator: "Understand French?"

It was Captain Prokovsky who replied, without moving his head: "We understand. We do as you order." His hands moved across the controls, and the blond man had to steady himself with his free hand against the back of the dead interpreter's seat as the plane started a sharp whining turn. The blond man leaned forward and began studying the bank of flickering luminous needles in front of the pilots; he knew which dials to look for, and checked their readings against the chart on the navigator's table. When he was satisfied that the new course was correct, he nodded to the French gunman and went back through the communicating door into the passenger cabin.

The sudden turn of the aircraft had upset most of the glasses of champagne, and the stewardesses were hurrying about the aisle with napkins. The blond man switched on the intercom and began speaking in French: "We are altering course. Our destination is temporarily changed. You will fasten your seat belts and not move." His words were the signal for four men, who had all been identified at the airport as accredited French correspondents, to stand up at regular intervals down the cabin and face the passengers, with their dum-dum pistols held loosely at the ready. They were all muscular Mediterranean types with that alert yet somehow emotionless look that is common to the rougher kind of policemen, to professional hoodlums, and to the more hardened breed of journalist.

The blond man spoke again over the intercom, this time in English: "You will remain calm. The plane has been commandeered, but no harm will come to any of you, providing you behave and obey orders. If anyone leaves his seat or attempts to take a photograph, he will be shot. The guns that my colleagues are holding do not leave clean or superficial wounds." While his French had been adequate, his English was perfect, with a flat clipped accent which several British correspondents recognized as South African.

Most of the genuine journalists remained calm, though agreeably shocked; their only real concern was the frustration of having to share such an experience with so many rivals. The Russian contingent looked either angry or glum; but no one appeared particularly worried, except the little Russian girl, who now dashed past two of the French gunmen and clutched the arm of the English journalist Fielding. Her apple cheeks were colorless, her eyes wide and wet, and she began babbling to him, first in Russian, and then, when he cut her short, in a burst of English: "Oh no, no, no! They take you! They take you!"

Fielding turned to her with a look of tired resignation, and muttered something, patting her hand. She began again in Russian, and stopped only when one of the gunmen approached; then wiped her eyes, turned, and walked bravely back up the aisle to her seat next to the two air hostesses, who sat mute and nervous, like waitresses during an embarrassing scene in a restaurant.

Fielding's neighbor, Ken Roskoe, had been listening alertly. "You know that girl?" he asked, his face forked with puzzlement.

"We know each other," the Englishman replied, with the same indifference that he'd shown to the girl.

"What did she mean—asking if they were taking you?"

"My dear fellow, I haven't the f-faintest idea."

Roskoe sat tight in his seat. "All those Intourist girls work for the KGB," he said after a pause. "You're not involved in all this, are you, Fielding?"

"I don't understand what you mean," said Fielding. "Unless you're implying that I'm involved in this hijacking, in which case I suggest you take a grip of yourself and stop panicking. We're all in this together, remember."

"But the girl?" cried Roskoe.

"The girl," said Fielding, "is an entirely private affair." And he closed his eyes.

From the back of the plane Pol had watched this episode between the girl and the English journalist with benign amusement. He now turned to her, in her seat opposite him, and repeated what Fielding had already told her. She still looked tense and pale, but the fear was leaving her eyes. "They won't take him away?" she murmured, in French.

"There is no cause for alarm, *ma petite*," Pol said, rocking gently forward in his seat. "No one will be hurt, if they do as they are told."

"But why? *Why?*"

Pol leaned across the aisle and gave her knee a little squeeze. "I promise that you will be back in Leningrad tomorrow."

"But these men with guns," she cried; and at the same moment the floor lurched steeply, and Pol, who had not yet fastened his seat belt, had to grab the corner of her seat to prevent his great weight from toppling to the floor.

The plane was losing height rapidly. There came a series of bumps, and several of the passengers winced and began blowing their noses to relieve the sudden change of pressure. In the control cabin the blond man was balancing on the sloping, shuddering floor, while a thick skein of blood jerked and zigzagged obscenely around his feet. Both pilots were braced against the controls, and the navigator was busily taking measurements off the plastic overlay. The blond man now took from his pocket a second chart and spread it out beside the one on which the Russian was working. It had a 1 : 100,000 scale, and showed the Finnish coast spattered with tiny islands, lakes, and lakes within lakes, and bulging peninsulas joined to the mainland by thin causeways. The area was full of villages linked by twisting roads to the coastal highway from Helsinki to Leningrad.

He laid a lean finger on a deserted point along the coastline midway between Helsinki and the Soviet-Finnish frontier town of Vaalima—a distance of some hundred kilometers. "We fly toward Lovisa, to this point between Borga Porvoo and Karhula. When we have reached latitude 62.5 you will commence a descent to one thousand meters. Understood?"

The navigator nodded, white-lipped. His hands shook as he picked up the pair of dividers, but the blond man took them from him and stabbed one of the points into the center of a ragged bay.

"This is the spot." He beckoned to Capitaine Duhamel and nodded down at the chart. "You will land precisely here, Capitaine. The ice will be up to a meter deep and covered with hard snow. You should have no problem."

The French pilot was smoking again; he said, without removing the cigarette, "We will be landing in the dark, blind."

"There will be flares."

"And the Finnish radar?"

"On your approach you will identify yourself to Helsinki and tell them you are losing height and may have to attempt an emergency landing. With luck we will be flying too low for radar." He looked at the altimeter needle and watched it creeping back around the dial—2000, 1500, 1200. "What is our exact position now?" he asked, turning back to the navigator.

The Russian indicated a point on the large-scale chart within a couple of centimeters of the dotted line marking the limit of Soviet territorial waters. The blond man turned to Captain Prokovsky.

"Captain, the moment you are contacted by Soviet ground or air reconnaissance, you will inform them that you are performing low-altitude exercises, and will shortly be heading south for Estonia. If you attempt to signal your destination, or raise the alert, you will be killed."

The Russian pilot nodded to show that he had understood, and hitched on his earphones. The blond man now turned to Capitaine Duhamel: "We are still flying parallel with the territorial limit?"

"Within less than ten kilometers of the military zone."

The blond man moved back to the chart and pointed to a complex of tiny offshore islands called the Haapasaari. "When we are exactly parallel with this spot, we will descend to two hundred meters and proceed due east and fly straight to the destination."

"And if we are intercepted?" said Duhamel.

"Do you think they will shoot down a planeload of their own government officials?"

There was a pause. "We are now within restricted military air space," Duhamel said, squashing out his cigarette under his heel. There was a quick crackle from Prokovsky's earphones. The Russian adjusted the mouthpiece, and the blond man leaned over him as he began

( 193

to speak, holding the barrel of his gun along the edge of the Russian's cheek.

Prokovsky repeated his message three times, then said in French, "I am being instructed to alter course immediately."

"How far are they?"

Prokovsky nodded at a flickering screen beside his knee, where two tiny green dots were beginning to appear. "Perhaps thirty kilometers," he said. "They are closing at over a thousand kilometers an hour."

"Turn due east," said the hijacker, "and drop to two hundred meters."

The Russian hesitated. Duhamel shouted: "This is madness! We cannot even see the water."

"Go by the altimeter," said the blond man; there was a note of bored contempt in his voice. "These planes are built to fly at a minimum of fifty meters—without radar. Tell your Russian colleague to inform the planes that we are having navigational problems."

The radar specks had grown into two bright green blobs that were now converging on the center of the screen. The floor bucked downward and sideways; the blond man braced himself against the back of Duhamel's seat and studied the second hand of his watch. He glanced at the navigator. "Twenty seconds. How far now?"

The navigator frowned. He was very pale. He said something in Russian, and Prokovsky repeated, "We are in Finland water in ten or fifteen seconds."

The green radar blobs had swollen into a large amoeba, and the first MIG-23 flashed overhead a couple of seconds later, followed by the other in close dovetail formation. Their lights broke apart, swirled upward in opposite directions, and vanished.

This time there was a furious crackle from Prokovsky's earphones, and the blond man ordered: "Tell them we are losing height and have engine trouble. But no May-day. Just break contact." His gun still rested against the Russian's cheek as the man spoke rapidly into the mouth-piece, this time with what sounded like a note of panic; then he wrenched the earphones off his head, switched off the R/T, and lay back against the headrest. He was grey and sweating.

"We are in Finnish territorial waters," said Duhamel, as the lights of the two MIGs came swooping down again, very close this time, and peeled away in the last second. The Troika-Caravelle's altimeter needle was trembling on the 200-meter mark. "We will be over Haapasaari in about thirty seconds," Duhamel added. "If we keep at this altitude, we have a good chance of hitting one of the islands." His face was suddenly taut with anger. "How many millions of francs are you asking, you dirty gang-ster?"

The hijacker nodded at the controls. "Pay attention to your work. As soon as we are over Hudofjörd, take us down to one hundred meters." He went on, grinning: "I heard that you are one of the best there is, Capitaine. You can do it. They might even give you the Order of Lenin."

Duhamel sat very straight, staring through the window into the blue-black darkness. There was cloud now, and a trace of ground mist; but still no wind.

Four minutes later a cluster of lights swept up into view, alarmingly high on their port side. Duhamel pulled back the stick and the floor rose with a shrill screaming vibration. For a moment the blond man almost lost con-trol, lurching back against the French gunman, who had not stirred from the rear wall of the cabin. The gun in his hand scarcely moved; it remained pointing between the heads of the two pilots.

A red glow now appeared directly ahead; then another; and beyond, a double row of orange flares, dully reflected off the frozen water. There were more lights from a village, racing past almost level with the plane as Duhamel now edged the stick forward, then pulled a lever and there was a shuddering howl as the nose cone came into line with the center of the flarepath, with the ground glowing red and green under the landing lights.

There was a bump and a soft scraping sound as the wheels plowed into the fresh layer of snow, then gripped the ice with a grunt, slewing to both sides as the weight of the aircraft settled, before pulling up with a long roar within less than a hundred meters of the last pair of beacons.

"You will remain here, you will not move," said the blond man. Duhamel was still staring stiffly ahead, his hands moving levers, touching switches, as the engines died with a slow moan through the arctic night. The blond man turned and went back into the passenger cabin.

One of the French gunmen had already opened the outside door at the rear of the plane, and a draft of freezing air swept up the cabin. Another of the gunmen had stopped beside Fielding, who had undone his seat belt and was already pulling on his coat and muskrat hat. The American, Ken Roskoe, stared up at him. "Hey, you going?"

"Yes, I'm going," said Fielding. He stepped into the aisle, with the gunman behind him, and walked down toward the open door. Five rows from the end there was a tiny click through the silence. A man in a suède jacket had snapped a Minox camera. He was just dropping it into his side pocket when the blond man leaped out and seized it from his hand, and in the same movement slashed the barrel of his gun across the man's mouth. The man screamed something that sounded like German, and sat down holding his face in both hands, with blood seeping between his fingers.

The only people in the cabin who now moved were Fielding and the French gunman. They reached the door, where the emergency chute had already been dropped out. The gunman was the first to go, holding the canvas taut, at a gentle angle, to take Fielding's weight. But at the last moment Fielding hesitated; he glanced at Pol, sitting almost opposite him, and the Frenchman gave him a quick grin, covering it almost at once with a red silk bandana with which he began to mop his face.

Fielding turned and clambered into the mouth of the chute. A moment later he slid out and sat down heavily in the snow. As he did so a pair of headlights flashed on and off out of the darkness, then came crawling toward them with a clank of snow chains. Behind them, beyond the last flares, lay a second pair of lights, dipped and stationary.

The car was a Volvo sedan with Swedish plates. There were two men inside. They drew up just beyond the wing tip and one of them got out. He was tall, in a fur hat and herringbone overcoat, and came walking briskly toward them. Fielding started to walk, too. The gunman followed a couple of feet behind, his hands thrust in the pockets of a quilted windbreaker.

Fielding stopped and said, "Good evening. I'm Fielding. Glad you could come."

"Geoffrey Donaldson," said the man. "It was no trouble at all." He was middle-aged, with a thin mustache and a generally military demeanor. He looked briefly at the gunman, then back at Fielding. "It's rather chilly—I suggest we get straight into the car."

Fielding glanced back at the plane, which was now in darkness, with the chute hanging limp from the door. Donaldson added, "We haven't got a lot of time."

Fielding followed him to the Volvo. Donaldson opened the front passenger door for him, and got into the back. The engine was running and the inside of the car was very warm. The man at the wheel nodded to Fielding and said, "I'm Brian Hughes. Hope you had a good journey." He had a smooth round face with tortoise-shell spectacles and an accent that at once suggested to Fielding more the commercial traveler than the officer and gentleman.

From the back seat Donaldson said, "I'm afraid our friend Wormold hasn't been having much luck with his vacuum cleaners. He's been meeting a lot of sales resistance."

Fielding smiled to himself: it must have rankled with London when he'd made them draw on Graham Greene's savage satire on the Service. Yet Donaldson had spoken without any irony or embarrassment. Perhaps he didn't have a sense of humor—or maybe he just wasn't much of a reader?

A second Volvo, this time with Finnish registration, drove past and stopped in front of the French gunman. Hughes had slipped into gear and they began to move forward.

"Did you get the Birkenheads?" said Fielding, turning to put his hat and coat on the back seat beside Donaldson.

"I'm sorry," Donaldson said, "but Robert Lewis tells me they can't get them any more. The Cuban government is standardizing all their brands of cigar."

Fielding nodded. "How long till they find the plane?"

"Not long. They're giving us a five-minute start. As soon as Pol's men are taken off, the pilot will raise Helsinki and they'll get the police out from Lovisa and Borga Porvoo. We'll no doubt pass the ones from Borga."

"What d-danger of someone identifying the cars?"

"Almost none. We were too far for anyone to read the numbers, and in this country almost every other car is a Volvo."

"Unless they set up roadblocks at once," Fielding muttered. He gripped the arm rest as the car bounced up a steep slope off the frozen bay, the chains screaming and churning a spray of snow and powdered ice, the back wheels sliding onto the level of a narrow track. "So what's the program?" he asked.

"The ferry leaves Helsinki in just over two hours," said Donaldson. "We should do it nicely."

"What ferry?"

"The overnight car-ferry to Stockholm."

"That wasn't the plan," said Fielding. "They promised a direct flight to Stockholm, then a car to meet me and take me to a safe house."

"That is precisely what is planned," said Donaldson; his voice was exasperatingly calm. "Only it was decided against a flight because of the highly changeable weather conditions at this time of year. You could be kept waiting at the airport for as long as it takes the ferry to cross. I suppose no one recognized you on the plane? None of the journalists, I mean?"

"I don't think so. But they'll remember me. And they'll

remember the gunmen. Only knowing Pol, he'll have laid on a private plane to collect them." He laughed bitterly. "I suppose that was too much for London? A false passport's routine stuff, but hiring planes costs money."

"It would also involve infringing Finnish air space," said Donaldson; "and London does not want to compromise the Finns more than is absolutely necessary. These things are very delicate."

"Don't flatter yourselves," said Fielding. "Delicacy doesn't come into it. It's just the old business of having to go through the proper channels."

"There were no proper channels," said Donaldson. "There never have been. If you must know, quite a few people in London are still very unhappy about the whole business. And a lot of others couldn't even be told. At one point London was insisting that the whole thing be handled by Pol."

"What made them change their minds?"

"London still has an interest in all this," said Donaldson stiffly. "Even you might appreciate that."

"Personally," said Fielding, "when it comes to the crunch, I'd as soon deal with an honest crook like Pol than a bunch of deskbound hypocrites in Whitehall."

"As you please," said Donaldson, and lapsed into silence.

Fielding groped for his hip flask, shook it, and found it was empty. Instead, he took out some cigarettes—a blue-and-white packet of Kazbeks. He tapped one out and was just pinching the hollow cardboard stem when Donaldson leaned over and said, "Try one of these." He offered him a packet of Rothmans. "And better give me that other one," he added. He took the Kazbeks from Fielding and opened his window just enough to throw the packet out. "A small detail," he added, "but it's so easy to become careless."

"Quite." Fielding smiled. "And it's nice to be looked after. But of course, you have to, don't you? Because London knows that if anything goes wrong, I can always break my side of the bargain, too."

Donaldson did not reply. They had left the narrow track along the peninsula, with the snowbanks reaching above the roof of the car, and now came out onto the Helsinki-Leningrad highway. The snowplows had recently been along it, but there was still a danger of black ice, and the chains kept their speed down to less than fifty miles an hour. There was no other traffic and no sign of the second Volvo. Hughes had made good time.

"We should have nothing to worry about," Donaldson said at last. "The ferry is Swedish, and passport control will be a mere formality."

"Even with a hijacked plane less than fifty miles away and all the hijackers still on the loose?"

"There will be a lot of confusion," Donaldson said smoothly. "And even with the journalists' descriptions, they can scarcely close every frontier post."

They were coming into Lovisa—rows of neat wooden houses with shallow, deeply eaved roofs thick with snow —like a toy town covered in cotton wool. Kim Philby was not quite home again yet, but he'd reached the garden gate and everything so far was spick and span, except for his passport in the name of Fielding.

Then miles beyond the town they ran into the first police. Two Volvos with spinning blue lights and sirens blaring passed them at a good seventy miles an hour; and a few moments later a convoy of grey vans and an ambulance raced past.

"How far now to Helsinki?" Philby asked.

"Another twenty minutes and we'll begin to join the city traffic," Donaldson replied. Besides the police convoy, they had seen only a couple of cars and a few trucks since leaving Lovisa.

"It shouldn't take them m-more than twenty minutes to get to the plane," Philby said nervously. "And I wouldn't put it past the Finns to order roadblocks in the center of the city."

For the first time Hughes spoke: "We're making a diversion to the port. They can't block every road."

"And anyway," said Donaldson, "even if Leningrad knows your alias, none of the journalists do."

Philby was sweating in the heat of the car. "I told one of them," he said hoarsely. "All right, it was bloody silly, but I thought you bastards would have the sense to hand me my new papers at once."

"Too bad for you," said Donaldson. "You can't blame London for everything."

Philby was thinking again of what Miss Galina Valisova had told him about last night on the Red Arrow Express and how the Australian had disappeared. He was sorry he'd had to leave Galina—she was a sweet little thing and he'd been quite fond of her. Pity she hadn't been able to keep a better eye on the Australian.

"Have you got something to drink?" he asked.

"You'll have to wait till the ferry," said Donaldson.

"I thought the Swedes were half-dry?"

"Their ferries aren't. Now relax."

Two more police cars sped past. The traffic was beginning to build up now, and they saw the lights of houses dotted about the flat black landscape. Hughes slowed into a suburb and they were stopped twice at traffic lights.

The glow of the city lay directly ahead, but Hughes now took a series of turnings to the left, down wide low streets, very clean and almost deserted; then a row of cafés behind misted plate glass; a building like a great plastic envelope turned inside out; the fairy lights of ships and the sweep of a prosperous, well-ordered modern port.

At 6:22 P.M., local time—seventy-eight minutes after the plane had touched down—Hughes stopped in front of a bar with a red neon sign in flowing script, *Haaklakuu-kima*. He got out, leaving the engine running, hurried through the double doors, and returned a few seconds later with a little man in a black raincoat and leather hat. The two of them got in without ceremony, the newcomer sitting in the back beside Donaldson and breathing hard, like an asthmatic. Donaldson said: "Give me your papers, Mr. Fielding."

Philby reached inside his jacket and noticed that Hughes' hand was in his side pocket. They weren't taking any chances, even now. Pol had been far more courteous.

Philby gave Donaldson a worn calfskin wallet; at the same time, the little man pulled out a brown envelope. Donaldson took it and sat weighing it in one hand, with Philby's wallet in the other. "Now empty your pockets, Mr. Fielding." Philby stared at him. "Don't argue," said Donaldson; he lifted a plastic bag off the floor and dropped the wallet inside. Philby handed him a collection of keys, matches, an old envelope, notebook, some loose change in kopeks, a Russian fountain pen.

Donaldson held up the bag and dropped each item in as though it were some ritual. "That the lot?"

Philby nodded. Donaldson handed the bag to the little man, who opened the door and got out. Donaldson pulled it shut after him, and Hughes eased the car out again into the traffic. Philby just had time to see the stranger disappear again into the café, clutching the plastic bag to his chest. He wondered if he were planning to sell its contents to the newspapers.

He held out his hand and Donaldson gave him the envelope. Philby slit the gummed flap and shook out a British passport, British and international driving licenses, a couple of sealed Manila envelopes, a plastic folder full of credit cards, two check books, a single-cabin ticket on the Jorgensen line to Stockholm, and a pair of clear-lensed spectacles.

He put on the spectacles and looked at the passport. Its cover had lost most of its gilt and its corners were soft and threadbare. It was made out in the name of Duncan Henry Saunders, British subject, born Sheffield, Yorks, 20.6.18; Profession, Businessman; Country of Residence, Great Britain; issued by the Foreign Office, 6 Sept. 1968; renewed 11 Sept. 1973, and valid until 6 Sept. 1983. The photograph was of a bespectacled, square-faced man in his middle sixties. Special peculiarities, nil. Only the signature was missing.

Inside were a number of West European entry and exit stamps, together with five *Binnekoms* and *Vertreks* from South Africa, and two Portuguese visas for Mozambique, one issued in London in November 1971, the other in Pretoria in April 1974. There were also valid vaccination certificates for smallpox, stamped by the Royal Borough of Kensington and Chelsea, and for cholera, on a yellow BOAC card. The back pages of the passport were full of T-form entries for sums varying between £300 and £500, issued by Coutts & Co., Cavendish Square, London W1.

The check books were from the Crédit Suisse, Geneva,

and from Barclays, Lombard Street, London, EC3. One of the sealed envelopes was from the Swiss bank, informing him that a numbered account, 4462481, had been opened in his name for the sum of 600,000 Swiss francs, with a covering letter introducing Monsieur Duncan Saunders *"To Whom It May Concern."* The second envelope contained two similar letters, one informing him that he had a current account of £2868.90 and a deposit account of £5960, both with Barclays' head branch in London.

"Satisfied?" said Donaldson.

"I'm worried about the signatures," said Philby. "Do Swiss banks usually open a numbered account without a specimen signature?"

"That matter has already been dealt with in your absence through previous correspondence. London Banking Section opened the account and explained that you were abroad and not contactable. An arrangement was made by which you present yourself in person, with your passport, to the Stockholm branch of the Crédit Suisse, and sign the specimen there. The same applies to the Barclays account."

The car had stopped. About fifty yards ahead were the ferry gates, under the illuminated sign JØRGENSEN. Donaldson leaned forward and handed Philby a ballpoint and a sheet of paper. "You'd better practice that signature before you sign the passport. You're going to have to get used to it."

Philby's handwriting was small and neat, and he had some difficulty simulating the fluent scrawl of a natural signature. After a couple of dozen attempts he settled for a flowing elision of *Dun-H-Sauers,* rounding it off with a flourishing *s.* His performance on the passport was not quite as good as the dress rehearsal, but it was adequate. "And I'd like some cash," he said.

"There were no arrangements for cash," said Donaldson. "However, I can probably lend you a hundred krone. That's nine pounds. And I'll need a chit from you. But we can deal with all that on the ferry."

Hughes had driven up to the gates, where a man in a blue uniform tore off part of their tickets. They drove on past two policemen with white peaked caps who just nodded, and were stopped by a man with gold tabs on his shoulders who glanced at their passports, read the number of the car, then waved them on to join a queue of cars waiting on the quay.

"When do we board?" said Philby.

"About now."

"You timed it well."

"Your French friend timed it well. Don't thank me for anything—not even the nine pounds."

"You haven't given them to me yet," Philby said, with a haggard grin. "You don't approve of me, do you, Donaldson?"

"I don't discuss personalities, Mr. Saunders. One gets used to all sorts in this business. Like doctors with sex."

A revolving blue light flashed through the rear window, coming closer. They were the last in the queue, and the police car stopped a few yards behind them. Four men in white caps got out; two of them carried sten guns. They came around the Volvo, two on either side, and one of them tapped on Hughes' window. Hughes rolled it down and a hard flat face with slanting eyes under the peaked cap said, "Passports!"

The three British passports were handed over, and the man outside passed them to a second policeman, who looked like an officer. Philby murmured to Hughes, "If they search us, and find that gun on you, don't expect any help from me."

Hughes flushed but didn't reply. The officer leaned into the open window and said, "Where you come from?"

"We've been staying at the Finlandia," said Donaldson.

The officer looked steadily at each of them for several seconds, turning to examine the photographs again in the three passports in his hand. "Hotel Finlandia?" he repeated. "Okay!" He thrust the passports through Hughes' window, and the four of them moved around the car ahead—a Mercedes with Swedish plates.

Three more vehicles pulled up behind the Volvo, as well as a second police car with another four men inside. It was nearly half an hour before the queue began to move onto the ferry. Hughes parked the Volvo on the lower car deck, and the three of them started up to the cabins, when two Suopos—plain-clothes Finnish Security police—stopped them at the top of the stairs and asked for their passports again. Philby blinked at them through his plain-lensed spectacles. The Suopos handed the passports back, and the three of them made their way to the main lounge. Philby hoped that Donaldson had been right about the bar.

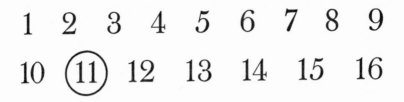
*Sir Roger Jameson-Clarke said: "I have never* had any great respect for your trade, Mr. Cayle. However, I accept that you're paid to do a job, and that is why you're here. And I may add that in this particular case you can consider yourself extremely fortunate."

"You sodding old hypocrite," Cayle said, with a grin. "You're bloody lucky yourself you haven't got twenty-five years! What frightened you off? Something I said in the Ritz? The title of the book I took to Philby? *The Confidential Agent?* That was the password and introduction, wasn't it? And the second book, *The Heart of the Matter,* was the green light. But you were already feeling the heat and had the good sense to skip when you heard I'd taken in the first book."

"I'm really not in the least interested in your speculations," said Sir Roger. "It has been agreed with my colleague here"—he nodded at the Russian who had brought Cayle to the room, and who was now sitting beside him—"that I should grant your newspaper an exclusive interview. I feel duty-bound to the British people, and to the world at large, to make certain of my views public. I am relying upon you to do an honest reporting job, and not to turn this matter into a vulgar, so-called spy scandal."

"I'll report exactly what you say, Sir Roger. But that won't rule out what other people will be saying. For instance, your link with Kim Philby."

Sir Roger Jameson-Clarke steepled his fingers together and stared at the ceiling. When he spoke he sounded tired and bored. "Philby seems to have become a nuisance to everyone. I wish to God we could forget him."

"Where is he now?"

Sir Roger glanced at the Russian, and paused. "We don't know," he said. "He left Moscow yesterday morning. He hasn't been seen since."

"Can't you keep a check on him?" said Cayle.

It was the Russian who answered: "Colonel Philby is a senior officer in the Committee of State Security. His present activities do not concern us." As he spoke a green light began winking on Sir Roger's desk. The Russian crossed to it in one stride and snapped down a switch. A voice crackled at him and he said, *"Harasho!"* and flicked the switch up again. At the same moment there was a tap at the door and a tall thin man in spectacles drifted across the carpet and laid a roll of Telex messages on the desk. The Russian read them standing, while the man waited behind him. Sir Roger didn't move.

The Russian gave an order and the thin man nodded and withdrew. For several seconds the room was quiet. Then the Russian spoke, addressing himself formally to Sir Roger: "There has been a serious incident over Finland. The Troika-Caravelle, on its demonstration flight from Leningrad this afternoon, has been forced to land near Helsinki. A Soviet member of the crew was killed, but there are no reports of any further casualties. However, an English journalist, who has so far not been positively identified, was taken off the plane by the hijackers. The hijackers have since escaped, without making any ransom demands." He looked straight at Cayle. "You still say you know nothing of why Colonel Philby arranged for you to travel to Leningrad last night?"

"Nothing beyond what I've told you." And before the Russian could answer, Cayle added: "Would I be out of line if I thought Kim Philby and that English journalist are one and the same?"

The Russian said woodenly: "The man was equipped with what seem to have been valid documents, including a press card issued, apparently, by the English newspaper the *Observer*."

Cayle began to laugh. "You've got to hand it to old Kim! He does have a sense of humor." He turned to Sir Roger. "Does this change things? For me, I mean? Do I still have your word that when our interview is over I'm free to leave?"

"You have my word," said Sir Roger Jameson-Clarke. Unlike the Russian, his expression was genial and relaxed; at least he would now be spared a long and bitter investigation into Philby's true loyalties over this last decade.

"Vladimir, I think we might now have some refreshments," he added.

The Russian walked stiffly over to the buhl cabinet and offered a choice of Western drinks. Cayle asked for Scotch-and-soda, and Sir Roger Jameson-Clarke had a gin-and-lime. The Russian drank nothing.

Cayle's interview with Sir Roger lasted three-quarters of an hour.

Roger Laval Pugh Jameson-Clarke had been recruited into the Soviet Intelligence Service, the GPU, in 1931 while he was reading Greats at New College, Oxford. He had never been a member of the British Communist party, but had remained, throughout his career in the British Diplomatic Service, an unflinching supporter of the new social and ideological order which had found its roots in

Soviet Russia. He agreed with Lenin that Russia had been ill-equipped to pioneer the Marxist revolutionary experiment, but the accidents of history had to be accepted, and their results shaped accordingly.

Sir Roger was a great believer in history. He explained the excesses of Stalinism as a historical lapse; but Stalin had had to be ruthless or the Soviet experiment would have failed as surely as the Chilean fiasco under Dr. Allende. Liberal democracy was a luxury that only a tiny percentage of the world could afford, or were indeed interested in. The Nazi-Soviet pact had not worried him: Stalin had been merely buying time, just as Chamberlain had, only Stalin had used his time more cleverly. Not only had he rearmed, but he had annexed the Baltic states as a vital buffer between himself and Hitler. Sir Roger had wanted Stalin to absorb Finland, too. Force had to be met with force, and Hitler had had to be beaten, and it had been the valor of the Russian fighting man—with more than seven million dead in combat—that had beaten him.

The only emotion that Sir Roger showed throughout the interview was when he recalled those English officers and diplomats, in their London clubs during the war, who had talked as though Britain were defeating Germany single-handed. "In comparison with Moscow and Stalingrad, the Battle of Britain and El Alamein were pillow fights!" he cried. Otherwise his discourse, delivered in a precise level tone, reminded Cayle of a bizarre mixture of muddled Utopianism and cold-blooded sophistry, of a fanatical old don and a rambling leader from the *New Statesman* of the thirties, with every so often the gleam of the Cromwellian ax—Sir Jolly Roger, stripped of his starched collar and chalk stripes, in his oilskins and pixie hat, the rogue sailor turned pirate, helping to command a ship he despised, sailing under the secret colors of a nation that wielded the brute power of the new Imperial colossus, and which fired the blue blood in Sir Roger's ancient veins.

For the man was a true Imperialist: he admired strength and order; he hated the flabby, insipid affluence of the West, the anemic Britain over which he had so long presided, with its permissive liberalism and tatters of colonial glory. For him, Hungary and Czechoslovakia had received the just deserts of renegade colonies. Imprisoned and persecuted writers and artists were spoiled, arrogant upstarts who presumed to set something called culture above manual labor. Why should a verbose novelist be held more important than a steel worker, a truck driver, a crippled war veteran, none of whom were ever awarded the Nobel Prize, showered with Western currency, or pampered by the world's press.

Cayle did not argue with him. He was a reporter, and he would report what Sir Roger said. He did try a few careful questions about the man's Oxford background, and who had recruited him, and how and where; but here Sir Roger was revealing nothing. Perhaps he had his own list of names tucked away in a Swiss bank vault, just in case the going got rough and the hounds began to close in.

At the end of the interview, Cayle asked: "How do you feel about leaving your family behind, Sir Roger?"

To his surprise, the man replied with enthusiasm: "My dear fellow, I couldn't give a damn. My conscience is clear, as they say. I have three grown-up children, none of whom I particularly admire. My first wife is dead, my second is safely married to a minor peer, and 'Bubbles'— my third—will just thrive on the notoriety. She may not get invited to any more royal garden parties, but they'll just love her in those appalling, fashionable clubs she likes going to. She might even make the international set. I've left her very well provided for, and I don't suppose they can take her title away—and even if they can, it won't stop her using it."

He poured them both a last drink. "I'm sorry I can't oblige you with a photograph, but that is strictly against the house rules." He raised his glass. "Here's to a safe journey home."

"One last thing," said Cayle. He glanced at Vladimir. "Dempster. Will I still be needed as a witness, if you catch him?"

The Russian shook his head. "There will be no necessity for that. We already have sufficient evidence against the man to shoot him many times."

"Perhaps—if you catch him. But you're not going to catch him, are you? You're not even going to try. Because Sergeant Dempster is your trump card. Kim still doesn't know that a certain group in MI5 have already tried to kill him—over here. In the West it's going to be a lot easier. As you said, having Kim quietly rubbed out will be a weight off a lot of people's minds—including yours. Even if he does bring shame and damnation on the heads of a few old stalwarts in Whitehall!"

"You overestimate him," Sir Roger said. "Philby is no longer important to us. A temporary embarrassment, perhaps, but we might call that quits. As a source of intelligence, he will be of very little use now to either the British or the Americans."

"Pol evidently doesn't think so."

Sir Roger gave a delicate shrug. "You imply that Pol engineered this hijacking over Finland? Well, perhaps, but I have no idea what a man like Pol has in mind for

Philby. All I can say is, neither of them is actively anti-Soviet."

"But you still wouldn't mind if Dempster was allowed to finish the job?"

Sir Roger shook his head. "I'm not going to be drawn on that one, Cayle." He finished his drink, then looked at his watch. "Your plane leaves in just over an hour. Vladimir has arranged for a car to take you to the airport. But one word of advice. You've been very lucky. You have broken Soviet law by entering the country without a correct visa, and have consorted, on your own admission, with a member of British Intelligence in London, for whom you have been running errands here on behalf of a criminal traitor." There was silence. Outside, big spangled snowflakes were drifting against the half-curtained windows.

"The Russians have a proverb—'you lower the bucket into the well twice, and the third time the rope breaks.' Even well-known journalists are dispensable."

Cayle felt a dryness in his throat. They were the same words that Dempster had used to him.

Vladimir stood up, and Cayle followed. "Good-bye, Sir Roger."

"Good-bye, Cayle. Remember me to the Squadron."

$$1 \quad 2 \quad 3 \quad 4 \quad 5 \quad 6 \quad 7 \quad 8 \quad 9$$

$$10 \quad 11 \quad \textcircled{12} \quad 13 \quad 14 \quad 15 \quad 16$$

*The ferry put into Stockholm at five next eve-*ning. The city and its network of islands were a watery blur through the winter rain, and Swedish Customs and Immigration weren't wasting time hunting for heroin or hijackers. Although Finland is next door to Sweden, it is not part of Scandinavia, and when a Franco-Soviet airliner gets seized over Russia and taken to Finland, it is no business of the Swedes—if the Swedes can help it.

Kim Philby had spent the hundred krone that Donaldson had lent him on a bottle of French brandy, which he'd finished after lunch; but they managed to get him down the steps and into the back of the car, and keep him awake while they passed through the landing formalities. The Swedish authorities disapprove of drunks almost as much as of hijackers.

They drove through the city center and stopped at the station, where Donaldson bought all the Swedish and foreign newspapers. In most of them the story had only made the stop-press; but the Swedish evening papers were carrying banner headlines. Philby woke up long enough for Donaldson to give him a quick résumé of the reports. The plane had been returned that day to Leningrad, with all the Soviet passengers aboard. The hijackers were described as being of suspected French or Corsican origin, with one who was probably South African. About the mysterious English journalist who had left the plane—

and had been disowned by his alleged employers in London—various theories were being advanced, including one that he was a dissident Russian intellectual. Charles Pol had been granting interviews to both the press and the Suopo, in which he talked of "the scandal of international brigandry" and how he would work and pray to see the pirates brought to justice.

So far no newspaper had mentioned the name Philby.

Philby went back to sleep as they joined the Autobahn north to Uppsala. Hughes drove fast for three hours through the sub-arctic twilight, stopping once for gas near the town of Avesta, where Philby drank a couple of cups of black coffee. Donaldson had told him they were going north to a little place near the Norwegian border called Medstugan. But Philby showed little curiosity; he didn't even ask to see it on the map.

At nine o'clock, when it was dark, they stopped for dinner in a pine-log restaurant where Philby and Donaldson shared a bottle of root beer. Philby seemed quite sober again and they ate almost in silence. There was nothing strained or artificial about their relationship: it was simply a matter of rank. In Finland Donaldson had been in command; he had even treated Philby with a certain impatient contempt. But once they reached neutral Sweden, Philby had taken on a new status. Donaldson now assumed a subtle deference toward him, as though he accepted that he and Philby were not on the same level, socially or politically. Hughes hardly spoke at all, even to Donaldson. He was merely the chauffeur.

When the meal was over, Donaldson paid, carefully folding the receipt into his wallet, and they got back into the car. For the next hour they passed through a flat wasteland of forest and frozen marsh, and at eleven they stopped at Östersun, on the edge of a large lake. It was cold and damp, with a stench of decayed tundra. Donaldson had already booked three rooms in the hotel. An old man with a face like a ball of brown string carried in their luggage, including the suitcase and overnight bag that Philby had been given on the ferry. The suitcase was of old pigskin, with silver-plated fittings and the initials DHS in faded gold, and was covered with hotel stickers from the President, Johannesburg, and the Polana, Lourenço Marques. Both cases had TAP airline tabs tied to the handles.

Donaldson put in a call for 6:45, said good night, and the three of them went to their rooms. Philby half unpacked, partly for convenience, and partly because he was curious to know what personality London had concocted for Duncan Henry Saunders, Esq.

The contents of the luggage, like the cases themselves, were expensive and in good condition: a leather toilet kit from Asprey's, a pair of ivory-backed hairbrushes, silk pajamas from Simpson's in Piccadilly, all monogrammed with his new initials; a hound's-tooth jacket, cavalry-twill trousers, cashmere sweater and a tartan-lined raincoat. There were also changes of socks and underwear, and four Turnbull and Asser shirts, size sixteen—his own. The overnight bag contained a rechargeable electric shaver, electric toothbrush, a half-empty bottle of Vetiver de Carven, the latest editions of *Time,* the *Economist,* and the *Investor's Chronicle,* and a jumbo paperback of Lawrence Durrell's *The Alexandria Quartet.*

Philby chuckled to himself. Duncan Saunders was a fastidious, well-to-do businessman with South African interests and middle-brow intellectual pretensions. He undressed and put on the silk pajamas, which fitted him perfectly. He was still very tired, and lay down under the quilt and was asleep almost at once.

At about four in the morning, Donaldson, who was in the next room, was awakened by a scream, followed by sobs. He leaped up and ran into the passage. The scream came again, from behind Philby's door. The door was locked. Donaldson hammered on it, and there was another sob, then Philby's voice, scarcely recognizable, crying what sounded like "The fishes! The fishes!"

Donaldson began hammering again, and calling, "Saunders!" in a loud whisper. There was silence. He stood back, wondering whether to kick the lock in, when there was a shuffling sound and the door opened.

Philby stood just inside, pale and sweating. Behind him, from the light in the passage, Donaldson could see the quilt lying humped on the floor at the foot of the bed. "What the devil's going on, man?" he asked, still in a whisper. "You'll have the whole place awake!"

"Sorry—b-bit of a nightmare." Philby swayed against the side of the door, and Donaldson saw there were tears in his eyes. "W-was dreaming about dead m-mermaids," he muttered, and tried to smile. "B-bloody silly. You haven't got a drink, have you?"

"I've got some Scotch," said Donaldson. "Stay there— I'll get it."

Philby had rearranged the quilt and turned on the bedside light when he returned. Donaldson fetched a glass and poured some whisky into it. Philby was sitting on the bed, breathing hard. Donaldson handed him the glass and waited until he had taken a drink, then said, "Just mermaids?"

"What?" Philby's eyes seemed to focus on him with difficulty. "Oh yes. I get them sometimes—when I'm over-tired. Had them since I w-was a child."

"Always about mermaids?"

Philby sat turning the glass around in his hand. "Not

always. This one was just silly. Fish eating dead mermaids." He looked up at Donaldson and this time his eyes were quite steady. "Ever seen a body that's been in the water a long time?" Donaldson didn't answer. "The police call them 'floaters.' They're worse than ordinary bodies."

"Have you seen one?" said Donaldson.

"N-no. But I've been told about them." He took a deep breath. "You know all about me, Donaldson, I'm a squeamish bastard. I don't like to see things hurt. Especially animals. And I hate dead things. When I go, I want to be cremated. I can't stand the idea of what happens in one of those bloody boxes."

"Do you need something to make you sleep?"

"Pills, you mean?" Philby shook his head and climbed back under the quilt. "I never take pills. And don't start feeding me any, either. That's not part of the deal."

"Good night," said Donaldson, and walked stiffly out. The door locked automatically on the inside.

They left next morning at seven o'clock, driving north again through the same flat forest landscape, broken by misty lakes and great stretches of tundra, like moldering patches on a white-dappled carpet. After two hours they came to a small town where they stopped at a café, and Hughes fitted on snow chains. The café was full of leathery-faced men in parkas and high boots; they looked like woodsmen or hunters. They turned together and watched Donaldson and Philby with suspicious pale-blue eyes. Donaldson, assuming his deferential manner, asked Philby what he would like, and Philby said, "Schnapps." Donaldson gave the order and was told they served only beer. He ordered two coffees and a beer for Philby. A few moments later they were joined by Hughes.

Donaldson kept looking at his watch. It was hardly the sort of place where they were likely to be greatly interested in a hijacking over Finland; but they'd remember three well-dressed foreigners asking for hard liquor in the middle of the morning.

A few miles beyond the town they joined a smaller, snow-covered road that led eastward into the fir-covered mountains. Hughes drove slowly and carefully. There was no traffic, and the snow was getting thicker, with ruts of rocklike ice. The sky had a grey glare that seemed to belong to no time of day. It was still too far south for the Midnight Sun, but the kind of place where day and night pass without variety, like the bleak unbroken landscape. A timeless place. A place as empty and neutral as the rest of Sweden, and even more dull.

Toward noon they crawled through a one-street town with single-story log houses heavy with snow—and just outside turned up a steep track around bends that twisted up between the tall endless fir trees, until Philby felt that familiar cold place in his stomach that he had felt many times before. Duncan Henry Saunders was going to ground.

The house was a wooden chalet with two floors and a garage. The fir trees grew so close to the door that there was almost no room in which to turn the car. They were let in by an old woman who looked like a witch out of Grimm. Inside, it was all stained pine, and so dark that the lights were on, although it was still only midafternoon. The rooms were small and full of heavy carved furniture. There were no books, and the only pictures were dim portraits of Christ in rusty metal frames.

Donaldson showed Philby into a room with a four-poster bed. "Come down when you're ready."

"I'm ready now," said Philby. He left his cases on the bed and followed Donaldson down into a long wooden room. A man turned, with his back to the stove, and held out his hand. "Mr. Saunders! I'm Thomas. How do you do?"

He was very tall and as bald as an egg. His face was almost translucently white, with a bluish pallor around the eyes. Philby found it difficult to guess his age, though he put him around ten years younger than himself. His voice had the languid self-confidence of a man used to giving orders, though unlike Donaldson there was nothing military about him.

"I expect you're ready for a drink?" he added, and turned to a large open dresser, well stocked with bottles. Philby asked for whisky, straight, and Thomas poured him tumbler three-quarters full. It was a gesture of hospitality that Philby was to get used to in the coming weeks.

"You'll be staying with us for about a month," Thomas went on, as they sat down in the stiff armchairs. "The exact time will depend on the progress we make. There is, as you see, very little to distract us. Major Donaldson will be leaving us tomorrow, and then we will have the whole week to ourselves. You should be quite comfortable. And Miss Meedla, our housekeeper, is very discreet. At the end of the week, if things go well, a man will be joining us from London. He will be concentrating on the technical details regarding your past—or, rather, Duncan Saunders' past." He gave a slight, deceptive smile. "We must make sure that Mr. Saunders becomes a man of substance—and not just financially."

"When do I get back to Stockholm to confirm the bank accounts?" said Philby.

Thomas lifted a bald eyebrow. "You won't be requiring any money while you're here, surely?"

"The money is simply your earnest of good faith, Mr. Thomas. That's all I'm interested in."

"The bank accounts are all in order, I assure you."

"But I don't sign them until you give the nod? In other words, if I don't co-operate, the accounts are canceled?" Philby glanced at Donaldson, who sat empty-handed, staring at the floor. "I imagine that if London could fix the accounts in the first place, they can always unfix them?" He gave them both a slack grin. "London seems to have improved while I've been away. They can no doubt fix a lot of things. Especially in the wilds of the Swedish-Norwegian border?"

Thomas frowned. It was like the creasing of rice paper; Philby almost expected the man's skin to tear. Thomas said: "There is really no point in being melodramatic. We promised you a 'safe house,' and this is it. I have no intention that it should be anything but safe. Now, Duncan—I shall call you Duncan from now on, to help you get used to it—when you've finished your drink, we might have something to eat? Then perhaps you'd like a little rest? Or we can start work straight after lunch."

"We can start now," said Philby.

"Fine." Thomas turned and called, "Miss Meedla!" The old crone appeared at once, as though she'd been standing outside the door. Thomas spoke to her in Swedish, and she grunted something and disappeared again.

"Don't worry," he said to Philby, "Miss Meedla doesn't speak a word of English."

Over the next week Philby spent an average of ten hours a day with Thomas. It was an arduous but ideal arrangement for a debriefing. There were no distractions, no recreations, except conversation and drink; and Thomas was generous with both. He showed no concern about Philby's drinking. Philby could drink what he liked, as much as he liked, when he liked. The hours didn't matter. Even the dull meals of ham, cole slaw, and canned fish were served to accommodate his drinking.

Sometimes he stayed up till the small hours, sometimes he passed out and woke before dawn, sometimes he began drinking early and slept half the day; but Thomas seemed always to be available, and although sober himself, he remained the perfect drinking companion—affable, responsive, patient. Occasionally, and only with Philby's agreement, he took notes. His questions were intelligent, well informed, and, above all, well timed. He never coerced or contradicted, never insinuated even a hint of doubt or skepticism; for Thomas was too experienced an interrogator to underestimate Kim Philby, even when the man was most drunk. Thomas knew just how far to push him, and just when to pull back; he never tried to trap him when he was drunk, and never made the mistake of assuming that Philby would have forgotten things when he was sober again.

Donaldson had left on the second day, but Hughes stayed on as a kind of batman-cum-butler, taking the car for the daily shopping in Medstugan, chopping wood for the stoves, and carrying Philby to bed when he was incapable of walking. There was no telephone in the house, but Philby guessed that there might be a short-wave radio —probably in the garage, which was always kept locked, even when the car was away. Philby never saw a newspaper or heard any news at all from outside; but far from complaining, he found the isolation restful, even stimulating.

Most of his sessions with Thomas were erratically informal. Philby's various masters had always admired his precise mind, despite its alcoholic lapses, and his phenomenal memory; but even he found it difficult to keep track of their daily progress; and sometimes it seemed that Thomas himself had lost the thread. One afternoon, after a heavy liquid lunch when Philby had been building up to a detailed picture of his activities in Washington after the war, Thomas suddenly suggested a break; and when they resumed toward evening, he began, instead, asking about Philby's financial difficulties after he'd been sacked by SIS in the wake of the Burgess-Maclean scandal. It was only next morning, almost casually, that Thomas brought him back to his contacts with the CIA.

At first these tactics puzzled Philby. For despite his innate contempt for Whitehall, he had never expected that they might send him an incompetent, or even an eccentric. Philby had agreed to co-operate with his former employers by supplying them with information, "in order to balance the books," as Thomas put it. But Thomas was not merely collecting the information—he was supposed to collate it, correct and tidy it, so that the final dossier to London would be complete and coherent. Why, then, this haphazard technique?

Philby decided that the clue was in his own drinking. At first this would have appeared to be the one advantage that Thomas had over him, but Philby's response to alcohol was so bizarre—his capacity to insulate certain compartments of his mind when drunk, and to recover his faculties both quickly and completely, were so notorious—that his state of mind while drunk became an actual disadvantage to anyone trying to evaluate the exact worth of his information. Thomas was combating this with his own erratic tactics, so that Philby himself would become confused, and could never be certain whether Thomas had really lost his way or was deliberately changing the subject.

An easier solution for Thomas might, of course, have been to withhold all alcohol from him during his whole stay; but Philby reasoned that Thomas wanted him in his natural state, without pressures or privations. Philby was not, after all, a prisoner, or even a reluctant collaborator. He was merely fulfilling his side of a bargain.

At no time did Thomas imply that he might have been lying or holding out on him. But there was one matter that was never even broached: the identity of Philby's former Communist friends and masters within the British Establishment. His silence here remained his guarantee against prosecution and possible elimination; and both he and Thomas knew that it was in their different interests that those names remain forever secret.

After the first four days, Thomas had exhausted Philby's career between 1944 and 1951; and the next two days were taken up with details of his career with the KGB. Here Thomas probed for every scrap of information, however trivial: he wanted to know the brands of cigarettes the various agents smoked, whether they had certain privileges, like being able to shop at the Beriozkas; what clothes they wore, what books they read, music they preferred; which were womanizers, homosexuals, drinkers, gamblers, insomniacs; what their home life was like and where they took their holidays.

London would know many of these details, and Philby was careful not to lie or invent the answers; if he didn't know, or wasn't sure, he told Thomas, and they passed on to the next question. The one other area that Thomas never touched upon was Philby's own life, his own habits, private preferences, and dislikes.

They were a tedious two days, and Thomas lightened them by producing a chess set. The weather was mostly bad, but even when it cleared, Philby was reluctant to go out. He drank heavily; and he talked all the time when he drank, but never about himself or his future plans.

Thomas' only indication that he was satisfied with their sessions was his announcement, at the end of the week, that the second man would be arriving from London next evening. The rest of that day was spent diagnosing the events that had led up to Philby's departure from the Soviet Union. It was only then that Thomas, during a full and accurate account of Cayle's conversation with Hann in the British Embassy in Moscow, described Sergeant Dempster's attempt on Philby's life.

"You're not out of the fire yet, Duncan—not by a long chalk. Of course, MI5 was acting illegally—quite outside its authorized territory. But that doesn't mean to say they aren't getting help, official or unofficial, from the powers on high. And threatening to expose everything you know won't necessarily help you in the long run. The Establishment's changed, you know. There's a lot of new blood come in, and they don't always have the same standards as the rest of us. You might even say, the Establishment's become fair game." He smiled wistfully. "But that's something I expect you understand?"

Philby's response was enigmatic; but by ten o'clock that night he was dead drunk and had to be carried to bed again by Hughes. Just after midnight he woke up screaming again, and Thomas found him cowering at the bottom of the bed, his silk pajamas soaked in sweat. He was sober, and Thomas gave him a whisky and hot milk, and left him. But he was worried. This was the same Philby they had cracked in Beirut; but it was no part of Thomas' plan to crack him again, here in Sweden.

He was even more worried when Hughes volunteered the details of Philby's previous nightmare, in the hotel on the way from Stockholm. Thomas had thought at first that Philby had been badly shaken by the news of Dempster; but when he thought more carefully about it, he realized that Philby must have anticipated some reaction of this kind. He was too old a hand to think that everyone in the Service would drop him like a chewed bone. Thomas was worried that there was something else on Philby's mind—something that only exploded in his subconscious, and which even the subtlest interrogation would be unable to uncover.

Philby had been responsible for the deaths of many men; he was a lifelong spy and a traitor twice over, and vain enough to be proud of it. He had also spent nearly half his life in danger of being discovered, by one enemy or another. Yet there was something on his mind that caused him, in this safe house in the depths of neutral Sweden, to wake in the night screaming and covered in sweat.

Thomas hoped that Philby was not, in a quiet, unobtrusive way, going mad.

The man who came from London was called Robin Horne. He was youngish, smooth-faced, and wore a blue bow tie. There was a discreet arrogance about him as he greeted Philby, without shaking hands. Men like Horne had a job to do, but it didn't include shaking hands with traitors.

( 229

He was very affable with Thomas, and spent some time chatting with him about obscure friends in London, deliberately ignoring Philby; then, almost as an afterthought, he took a plain green folder from his briefcase and said, "Oh, by the way, Saunders, you'd better start studying this. You're going to have to know it by heart."

The folder contained over a hundred foolscap pages of double-spaced typing: the potted biography of Duncan Henry Saunders, with every detail from his background, including his career in the City of London, when he had gambled on copper in Northern Rhodesia and made a quick killing. But he had been slow at reading the African political forecasts; and on 11 November 1965 he had waked up to find a fair slice of his wealth frozen in the new independent state of Rhodesia.

Saunders was today a semiretired gentleman of means and easy charm, and a good social mixer. He could spend money freely—though not so freely as to attract attention. In Rhodesia, Horne explained, wealthy English expatriates with Exchange Control problems enjoyed a special status; and Duncan Saunders was very much one of the old school of Englishmen: bit of a bastard where the women were concerned, drank a bit too much, gambled a lot, especially at backgammon and on the horses, but a good sort really. Very keen on cricket. And his politics were dimly to the right of center, with no time for any claptrap about Africa for the Africans. "One Man—One Vote—Once," was Saunders' stock reply to a silly question.

"You're not an intellectual," Horne told him, "but you're not stupid either. If you meet someone down there with brains, don't be afraid to treat him as an equal. There are still a few bright people left in white Africa, and they're not all in the money markets. But don't talk too big, or be too reticent. And on no account give the impression you've got a shady past. You're not bent, remember. You've had your ups and downs, and the downs have been mostly due to taxation and Labour governments. As far as local politics are concerned, distrust the blacks, but don't hate them. Play everything strictly down the middle, at least for the first few months."

Thomas was rarely present at these sessions between Philby and Horne. And unlike Thomas, Horne quickly insisted on a severe daily routine, which greatly restricted Philby's drinking habits. After they had established Saunders' background and character, Horne took him through an exhausting study of both the political and the social climate of White Africa.

Philby himself had never been south of Egypt, but he would now have to learn as much about Africa as Duncan Saunders knew: a well-to-do Englishman who liked to winter in the sun, with plenty of servants and drinks by the pool, and rounds of cocktail parties where they talked cricket and rugby.

"White Rhodesia's got the same population as Leicester," said Horne, "and a lot of the same sort of people. Small-time Midland businessmen and shopkeepers who've emigrated into big houses, and do everything to keep up with the neighbors, even if it means making do with a secondhand Toyota and local gin, so they can afford an extra houseboy to keep the front lawn trimmed and the swimming pool clean. If you mention Kafka, they won't know what you're talking about. They'll think Van Gogh's a South African politician, and if you bring up Graham Greene they'll think you're either an intellectual snob or a subversive. They're stupid, bigoted, and they long to be loved. But they're also getting to hate the English, or what they think of as the English—a nation of strike-happy, long-haired degenerates.

"But however stupid you find them," Horne added, "always remember one thing. They've got one of the most efficient Security forces in the world, and probably the only one that is against both the CIA and the KGB, not to mention us. That might be an advantage to you. But whatever else you do, never underestimate them."

"It sounds like Darkest Surrey," Philby said, "without the wife-swapping parties."

Horne didn't smile. He pointed to the green dossier. "I suggest you spend the rest of today and tomorrow studying that. I want you to know it so you can tell me how many 'distinctions' you got in your school Certificate, and what was the name of the cruise ship you first took to Cape Town, and who were the members of Boodle's you used to win money off at backgammon."

"I'm not a backgammon player," said Philby.

"That's another thing you're going to learn before you leave. I've got a board with me." He said good night and left.

Philby fetched a fresh bottle of whisky and began to read. His mind was exactly suited to the dreary task, and even as he drank into the night, he retained the most minute, even frivolous details. He learned them as an actor learns his lines, repeating them as he fell asleep, and by morning he could recite them in any order, without a mistake.

When Horne came down to question him, Philby passed, word perfect; and although Horne was loath to show it, he was impressed.

One detail troubled Philby. It concerned Saunders' blocked bank account in Rhodesia. Philby assumed that such an account must exist. Indeed, the necessary documents, with which Horne had provided him, all looked convincingly genuine. Either the account had been opened before 1965, in which case London had been anticipating the operation long before Pol came on the scene; or somewhere there was, or had been, a real Duncan Saunders.

One evening, while they were playing backgammon, Philby asked: "Is he dead? Or on ice?"

"I'm afraid I'm not in a position to answer that," Horne said. "The fact is, I don't know. And I probably couldn't find out if I tried. All such matters are dealt with through Personnel and Banking Section. Does it worry you?" he added, throwing a double. He was winning the ninth game that evening.

"I'd just like to be sure that the real Saunders doesn't pop up, like the ghost at the feast, during some rowdy barbecue party while I'm getting friendly with one of van der Byl's bedfellows, that's all."

"You need have no fear of that," Horne said, with a complacent smile, and won the game.

"I was only asking," Philby said lightly. "And I haven't asked very much so far."

"No," said Horne. "You've been very trusting."

Philby stayed at the house near Medstugan for thirty-three days. At the end of them his debriefing was complete; his *alter persona* of Duncan Saunders had been instilled in him like an actor taking on a leading role that he knew he would be playing for at least a year; and his new mission in life, at the age of sixty-five, had been planned to the last detail. He had even grown a short grey mustache.

At 10:30 on a bright April day in Stockholm, a plump, well-dressed Englishman walked into the offices of the Crédit Suisse on Kindstugaten and asked to see the manager. He showed his passport and two letters of introduction.

Forty minutes later Harold Adrian Russell Philby, alias Duncan Henry Saunders, crossed the Slottsbachen and entered the Kreiskaffe on the corner, to have a farewell drink with Thomas.

For the first time in his life Philby found himself with plenty of money to spend; yet what he wanted most he could never have: the three thousand books, none of them very valuable, that he had collected over the years and abandoned in his flat in Moscow. He also wondered who would be taking care of Donald and Guy. They wouldn't be getting any whisky in their milk every morning, that was for sure. There were some things that even a Swiss bank account couldn't buy.

*Cayle had been lying low for five weeks.*

He had flown out of Moscow on the last night plane, an hour after leaving Sir Roger Jameson-Clarke, and had broken his journey in Copenhagen, where he'd checked into the airport hotel and put through a personal call to his editor at home. He gave him the gist of the story in a couple of sentences, which were enough for the editor to forbid him for the moment to put foot back in Britain. Instead, he ordered him to catch the first morning flight to Paris and meet him for lunch in a little restaurant off the Rue Saint-Honoré.

Cayle had already told his story, in varying lengths, to three different people in two days—Dempster, Hann, and Sir Roger. He now wanted a quiet lunch with the editor with plenty of time for them both to think; so he had stayed up half the night typing a wad of notes, which he handed to the editor as soon as they met in the restaurant. He left them with him while he himself concentrated on the *quenelles de brochet* and a good Sancerre. The notes would form the basis of both the published interview with Sir Roger and any supporting story that the editor might decide to run.

The editor read them through twice, eating slowly with his left hand, and by the middle of the *poulet de Bresse* he had made up his mind. "I'm going to stick my neck out on this one, Barry." He took off his spectacles and tucked them behind the folded handkerchief in his breast pocket. "I'm going to assume you're telling the truth. A lot of people won't. Or, rather, they'll say the story's a plant. But there's nothing here on Jameson-Clarke to contravene the Act. On the other hand there's nothing to authenticate the interview, except your word. We can assume that Sir Roger was acting on the highest authority. The KGB probably knew that Philby was planning to skip, and that he had a good chance of getting away with it. Wheeling Sir Roger into the limelight will be one way of distracting attention and claiming a little extra bonus from an embarrassing situation—that is, always assuming that the Russians expect Philby himself to come into the open, which—from what you tell me—I rather doubt.

"Now." He smoothed the hair down behind his ears and sucked in the corners of his mouth in a thoughtful pout. "I'm not just putting my head on the block, Barry. I'm putting yours on, too. By tomorrow afternoon the proofs will be out and so will the hounds. So I don't want you stepping out at Heathrow, all ready to be interviewed and possibly detained. I want you out of my hair. Lost. In a lonely little spot which only you know about. Preferably here in France, because the French are rather less keen to co-operate with the Foreign Office than most friendly countries—unless it's an extraditable offense, which in this case, of course, it won't be. That's not to say," he added, "that the British authorities are going to like you and me one bit after Sunday. As it is, I shall no doubt have to fight our own upstairs brigade every inch of the way when I get back. But the story's going to appear, don't worry. As for the follow-up—" He let his fork hang in mid-air. "It all really depends on what chance there is of Philby still contacting you. If Hann believed you, Philby will know by now—or pretty soon—

what happened on the train, and why you weren't at the airport in Leningrad. The question is: do we quote Sir Roger's KGB friend, Vladimir, and claim that Philby was the Englishman who was taken off the plane in Finland?"

"If we don't, someone else will—eventually."

The editor shook his head. "I don't think so. Where's the connection unless someone tells them? I hardly think Philby or Pol will, and the Russians certainly won't. As for anyone having recognized him, there are very few Western journalists who've seen him in the flesh since he defected. No, Barry. We sit on this one. My guess is that Philby, and the people who've got him out, will want time to breathe. Philby hinted to you, I think, that if he did get out, he wanted you to write it up—but not before he said so."

Cayle nodded. "I was to be his faithful Boswell and record the final chapter of his inglorious life, as he put it."

"Well, assuming he still wants you—for whatever operation he and this Frenchman are setting up—he may read into your silence the fact that you're still willing to go along with him. Are you willing?"

"I'm still on the story, aren't I?"

The editor's face was blank. "It's a slight chance, but I think it's worth it. Write up a full-color piece on the background to your interview with Sir Roger—how you first met him at Cowes, then short-circuited your visa and played the sick-act, and how you got picked up and taken to Dzerzhinski Square. Write it straight, and don't worry if it reads like a thriller. Most of your stories do. But leave Philby out of it. And leave out Hann and Dempster and any mention of MI5 or 6. I'm not scared—I just want to stay out of prison."

"How long do I have to keep my head down?" said Cayle.

"That depends on what happens after Sunday. If the heat stays on, I may have to send you on a slow-burning story like Portugal or the Middle East again. But my guess is that if Philby wants you, he'll make contact, through us, within the next month or two. From what he said to you, it sounds as though he not only wants recognition for this one, but instant glory, too. He won't be overanxious to start recruiting another journalist at this stage. And if we play right by him, he may well come back to you."

Cayle's head was growing muzzy with wine and his eyes stung from lack of sleep. The editor ordered coffee and cognac. "Any idea where you'll be staying?" he added.

"I've got a chum who works for Magnum and has a place down in the Auvergne."

"You can stay with David tonight and get some rest, then start tomorrow. But don't stay in any hotels. And let the office have a PO number where you can be reached. I don't want to know the address. Just drop a postcard and sign it 'Basil.' "

"Why Basil?"

"Because I like Basil. In my lighter moments I often think of you, Barry, as a latter-day Basil Seal. I'm an Evelyn Waugh fan."

"Like Kim's a Graham Greene fan," Cayle sneered. "I think we're both getting pissed."

"I didn't get much sleep myself last night," said the editor, folding his napkin. "I'm going to ring David now and tell him to get round to the flat and expect us."

It was much as the editor had predicted. The story appeared in the first edition on Saturday night, and by early morning had been taken up by every other British Sunday paper as well as radio and TV. It pushed the faltering mystery story of the hijacked Troika-Caravelle to the inside pages, and by Monday it was leading most of the press in the non-Communist world. The Foreign Office issued a pithy statement that neither confirmed nor denied the story, and Moscow was silent.

The editor gave a two-minute interview on BBC News, saying that he was satisfied as to the veracity of the interview, though he declined to divulge Cayle's immediate whereabouts "for professional reasons." There were some rude off-stage noises about the ethics of quoting the views of a confessed traitor; and at least one iron-ribbed backbencher rose in the House to accuse Cayle and the editor of being stooges of the KGB.

Meanwhile, with nothing to go on but Sir Roger Jameson-Clarke's diffuse speech to Cayle, a frenzied delight seized press, politicians, and public alike. Philby had been bad enough, but at least he'd been slightly bohemian and a heavy drinker. Blake had been half Jew, half foreigner; and Burgess and Maclean had both been alcoholics and homosexuals. But here was Sir Roger Jameson-Clarke—a frequent visitor to the Palace, the silver-haired, silken-tongued stanchion of the Establishment, and a member of the Royal Yacht Squadron Club to boot! It had been bad enough having a Soviet spy in the Athenaeum, but the Squadron was unthinkable.

So, with the frenzy came the rumors. No name was too high or too revered to escape suspicion, innuendo, even criminal slander. But there were no dramatic resignations; and the men on the Front Bench remained mum, as did the mandarins of Whitehall.

And Barry Cayle cooked his food on a Primus stove and went for long walks over the rocky hillsides around Rodez, trying to decide whether to get on with the novel that had started it all, or to wait until he heard from Philby. Every morning he called at the local post office on his way back from the bakery; but apart from a couple of bulky envelopes containing his forwarded mail, which consisted mostly of overdue tax demands and summonses for parking offenses, he heard nothing except for a short note from the editor: "Patience is a virtue. If you need more money, wire David."

After five weeks, and in a mood fluctuating between torpor and desperation, he put through a collect call to the editor. His master was not pleased. Cayle had broken their iron rule, by which he was always to telephone the private number of the Paris correspondent, who would then call London and arrange for the editor to put through a person-to-person call to Cayle, at the main hotel in Rodez. The editor had explained that this was a minor precaution in case the paper's phones were being tapped, in London, or Paris, or both.

"Just be a good boy and sit tight," said the editor. "If your hunch is right, he'll summon you, don't worry."

In the event, it was another two months before the summons came, and in circumstances that even Cayle could not have foreseen.

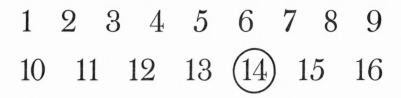

1  2  3  4  5  6  7  8  9
10  11  12  13  (14)  15  16

*From his marble perch high above Lake Geneva,*
Charles Auguste Pol watched the midnight-blue Mercedes
600 slide out of the tunnel of cypress trees and swing
around on the gravel forecourt below him, before disappearing into a garage somewhere in the lower reaches
of the white mock-Moorish villa.

Pol creaked slowly back and forth in his rocking chair,
shaded by a trellis heavy with green grapes. He was
loosely wrapped in a massive silk dressing gown pat-
terned with flame-eating serpents, while on his feet were
two tiny pink satin slippers. A bottle of champagne stood
beside him in a silver ice bucket.

A couple of minutes after the car arrived, he heard
footsteps on the patio behind him. He did not turn, but
waited until Philby reached a second rocking chair, then
flapped a soft hand at the champagne, his teeth gleaming
a roguish welcome. "So? Any results?"

Philby sank down with a crackle of wicker. He was no
longer wearing his lensless spectacles, and his upper lip
was again clean shaven; and although he had put on
weight during his stay with Pol, he looked tired and pale.
He ignored the champagne.

"Ah, but of course!" Pol cried. "The Krug is bad for
your heart. You'll have your usual cocktail? Peters!" His
fat fingers made a surprisingly loud snap, and a third man
glided out of the shadows of the patio and stood motion-

less behind the two chairs. He was lean and hard, in a suit the color of dried mud, with tight curly blond hair and a thin, clean scar down his right cheek.

"The usual for Mr. Philby," Pol ordered in French, without moving his head. The blond man turned and walked silently away in his crepe-soled moccasins.

Philby sighed. "Well, they've bitten—at last."

"You're certain?"

"Ninety-nine per cent. A white BMW outside Geneva. Picked us up outside the old League of Nations Building and stayed with us on the autoroute till Peters managed to lose them just beyond the Nyon intersection."

"There was no chance of your making a mistake?" said Pol.

"I'd say it was more a question of *their* making a mistake. And they'd hardly do that with a car like yours."

"Did you see them?"

"Peters recognized one of them from two days ago. He took a Polaroid snap of them while they were parked in Vevey."

Pol cocked an eyebrow. "More than one?"

"Two." Philby glanced around as the blond man, Peters, appeared at his side and handed him a thick frosted glass with a straw.

Pol drank some champagne and chuckled; then again, without turning his head, shouted: "Peters! The photographs, Peters."

Peters withdrew, and returned less than a minute later with two buff envelopes. From each he shook a shiny color photograph showing an identical street scene, taken in poor light, with cars parked along the curb facing the camera. Philby studied them both carefully. In each picture the second car along was a white BMW with only half the number plate visible; but it was enough to see that it was a foreign *Zollamt* registration. Both pictures also showed two men in the front seat. The driver looked young, sandy-haired, nondescript. Beside him, half hidden by the car in front, was a broad, chunky-faced man in wrap-around dark glasses.

Philby hesitated, compared the pictures, then handed them across to Pol. "I can't be certain—not without seeing the man in the flesh. The only reference I've got is an old mug shot I once saw in the *Zapiski*—that's the KGB central archives. They contain files on over eighteen million foreigners, including all known or suspected enemy agents."

"But you think you might recognize this one?" Pol jabbed his thumb at the top photograph in his lap, indicating the broad man in dark glasses.

"As I said, I wouldn't like to swear to it," said Philby, and took a long drink. "But if it's the man I think it is, he's called Sergeant Dempster—William Michael Dempster, officially attached to the Special Branch. That's the section of the British police that deals with political and subversive activities. Unofficially, he's what you would call a 'gorilla,' or a muscle man for MI5—the branch of British Intelligence engaged in internal counterespionage."

"Which seems to indicate that he's operating above and beyond the call of duty?"

"It means," said Philby, "that they're scraping the barrel, or they'd be using their regular thugs from MI6—the foreign section of the Secret Service."

Pol nodded slowly and sipped some more champagne. "I foresee a small problem. The Mercedes is registered with one of my French shadow companies. But if this man —this sergeant of the British police—can call on the services of British Intelligence, or at least certain members of it, it will not take him long to track down the car to me. Now don't misunderstand me—I have no reason to fear the British Secret Service. But I don't want those clumsy Swiss oafs coming up here and asking all kinds of damnable questions. That's one reason I bought this place—as a retreat, a haven of peace in an angry world."

"One thing I can assure you," said Philby: "In this case —in my case—British Intelligence is operating with very little rope. And this sergeant's now at the end of that rope. The plan seems to have worked, Charles. Three weeks cooped up here waiting, and now the bastard's ready to strike. He had his big opportunity back on the Red Arrow Express, and finished up getting lumbered with that damned great Australian journalist. His bosses in Whitehall won't have been too happy about that. If my guess is right, this'll be his last chance."

Pol drained his glass, glanced at his watch, then, with a agility that always amazed Philby, he bounded up on the balls of his slippered feet and came striding around the chair with arms outstretched. "It will be dark in one hour, *mon cher*. I estimate that if your English friend is to be given his last chance, you should hurry. Peters, have the car ready." He turned back to his chair and poured himself another glass of champagne.

"You're not coming?" said Philby.

"One fish is enough!" He giggled. "Besides, I'm too old for amateur heroics." He looked up as Peters, who had already left at Pol's earlier command, now reappeared in the archway to the patio.

"Monsieur Pol, there is a telephone call for you from Geneva."

Pol gave a gesture of dismissal, slopping champagne over his loose sleeve. "Tell them to call back."

"The gentleman said it was most urgent," Peters said, in his pedantic French, which betrayed a clipped South African accent.

Pol turned and for the first time looked directly at him. "All calls I receive are urgent, Peters. Did this gentleman give his name?"

"Yes, monsieur. Marmut."

Pol frowned, then gave Philby a quick beady stare, and without a word waddled away into the darkness of the villa. Philby glanced at Peters. "Marmut? Sounds like an Arab name."

"There are a lot of Arabs in Switzerland, sir. Rich ones, too. They find it a good place to keep their money, now that London's going bust."

"You don't like the British, do you, Peters?"

Peters turned to him, and for a moment a small dead-eyed smile crossed his face—or perhaps it was just the slightly crooked wince where the scar tissue met. "I keep my likes and dislikes to myself, sir." He swung on his heel and disappeared through the arch.

Philby stared after him, frowning. His innate sense of rank and authority had been mildly offended at the South African's manner: Johann Peters, formerly of the Transvaal Special Police Reserve, was Pol's chief retainer—a cold, brutal, obedient hireling who was paid to do only what Pol told him. His thoughts and opinions were as inscrutable as his closed, scarred face. Philby found him repulsive.

Pol returned five minutes later, mopping his brow with a monogrammed handkerchief, although the villa was fully air-conditioned. "You haven't left yet?"

"I was waiting for you," said Philby.

Pol gave a mischievous grin. "For a man who has lived for all his life on the edge of a precipice, you've come to need me like a nursemaid! Or perhaps a guardian angel? Now, you must hurry."

"Good day, Charles." Philby made his way down a series of marble corridors and shallow winding stairs that opened onto the gravel forecourt. The six-door Mercedes, which reminded Philby of a Stuttgart dentist's waiting room on wheels, was parked at the foot of the steps, with Peters at the wheel. Philby got in beside him, and the car sped forward down the narrow road between the cypresses toward the Geneva-Lausanne autoroute. As usual he felt no compulsion to chat with Peters, who was a fast but highly skilled driver; and for most of the fifteen miles to Vevey he was left to his thoughts.

At the first intersection on the autoroute, indicating MONTREUX 2 kms, Peters turned off and began a giddy corkscrew drive down the steep ramp leading to the lakeside. Philby found himself wondering about Pol's extraordinary background: anarchist freebooter in Spain, where he had ransomed one of Franco's generals for a hundred political prisoners; sentenced to death in Barcelona and escaped disguised as a priest; highly decorated member of the Resistance who had settled down after the war to run a supermarket for ladies' undergarments behind the Gare Saint-Lazare; leader of a clandestine mission for De Gaulle's Police Parallèle against the OAS in Algeria; later involved in shady gold and opium deals in the Far East; now comfortably established as an international financier with what he called "an excellent tax position overlooking Lake Geneva."

Reluctantly—and with a familiar sense of frustration—Philby concluded that he and Pol were very much opposite sides of the same coin: vain, devious, extravagant adventurers, with childish ideas that were half honest, half a sham to cover their playful machinations against authority. Their one obvious difference was that while Pol indulged himself with silk suits and champagne and luxurious limousines, Philby was content with a patched jacket and frayed tie, and whisky out of anything.

However, Pol's sustained interest in Philby was an enigma in itself, and the possibility that Pol had claimed some stake in Philby's future activities in Africa was something that fired Philby with less than enthusiasm. But Philby had one fatal weakness: he loved adventure; above all, he loved the uncertainty and mystery of adventure; and the more mysterious and uncertain became Charles Pol's motives and maneuvers, the more firmly and irrevocably was Philby drawn to him.

Peters had now slowed the Mercedes into the oncoming evening traffic out of Montreux.

Philby said casually: "Any idea where we're looking?"

"The car I photographed two days ago was parked outside the Hotel du Lac." Peters' eyes remained steadily on the road as he spoke. "And if you remember, it was in the same place this morning when it picked us up and followed us onto the autoroute."

"Let's just hope we're in luck this time," said Philby. He spoke with an infectious excitement, like a schoolboy.

Peters drove the length of the street, turned in a square, then started back, very slowly. Several other cars honked at them impatiently, and a big Citroën with French plates accelerated past them and cut in dangerously to avoid a truck. Only Peters' instantaneous reaction saved their offside fender. Not a muscle in his face moved. After a moment he spoke, deadpan: "It's behind us. Three—four cars back."

Philby turned and saw a white BMW 2500 sedan cruising on the outside of the traffic, about fifty yards behind them. "Pull up at this tobacconist's," he said.

Peters obeyed, double-parking the huge Mercedes in the full flow of the traffic. Philby ignored the blaring sounds and flashing lights, paused for a moment on the pavement, as though to check that he had his wallet, gave a casual glance back up the street, then entered the shop and bought a packet of Gitanes. When he came out, the traffic had again begun to move, except for the BMW, which had pulled into a space six cars back, parked crookedly, with its front wheels locked hard left and its engine idling.

Philby began to stroll down the pavement in its direction. The street was now filled with that flat neutral light just before dusk when distances and color are deceptive. Several cars had already switched on their side lights. He calculated that both the crowds and the visibility would make it unlikely for them to risk taking a shot at him.

He passed within a foot of the BMW and recognized the driver from Peters' photographs: a sallow, freckled face. The man beside him had on a blue beret, black leather jacket, and wrap-around glasses with reflecting silver lenses. There was a map spread across his knees, but he was looking out at the street. Philby came close enough to notice the lumps of muscle under the man's cheekbones, and to see that the map was a large-scale one of the Vevey-Montreux area. Then the man moved his head a fraction, and Philby caught a double glimpse of himself in the reflecting lenses, before walking on.

Twenty yards up the street he stopped at a newsagent's and bought a *Daily Telegraph*, then sauntered back, unfolding the paper and glancing at the headline: BIG SECURITY SHAKE-UP IN WHITEHALL. Neither the Mercedes nor the BMW had moved. He walked straight past the BMW without glancing at it this time, and could hear its engine still running. When he reached the Mercedes he refolded the paper and climbed in beside Peters. "It's the same two you photographed. Let's go."

Peters hesitated. "Is it the British policeman you were talking about, sir?"

Philby nodded but said nothing. Peters had started the engine and now pulled leisurely out into a break in the traffic. He drove at a measured pace, gathering speed only as the road widened out of town, back toward the autoroute. For a moment there was no sign of the BMW. Philby began looking out for it, but Peters, again with uncharacteristic familiarity, said, "Better not turn around, sir. No point in alerting them unnecessarily."

From then on Philby relaxed. They went around a traffic circle, and Peters touched the accelerator. At the turn to the autoroute Philby instinctively began to fasten his seat belt; and as they swung around the first bend he caught a glimpse of the BMW, about two hundred yards behind. He was almost beginning to enjoy himself. The fact that the hard-liners in MI5—or whatever establishment they now drew their pensions from—were using Sergeant Dempster for the second time suggested that it was a relatively local and limited operation, which in turn meant that Dempster's bosses must be getting desperate. Philby smiled to himself. No wonder Sergeant Dempster had had so little trouble getting out of Russia! Why pay two men to do the job of one?

They'd reached the intersection, and Peters slowed to allow two cars to pass on the inside lane, long enough to fasten his own seat belt—something, Philby noted, that he had never seen him do before, even while driving well above the speed limit on the crowded autoroute in from

Lausanne. At the same time, the South African turned to him and said, "Sit well back, sir."

The engine gave a low roar and they leaped into the fast lane. Peters switched on the lights, and Philby could see the needle on the speedometer creeping around the dial to 130—150—170— The dusk was deepening and the lake was a pool of mist on their right with the lights of Montreux winking up at them from about three miles ahead.

The needle was quivering just about 200 as they flashed past the blue-and-white sign to Montreux Est. The traffic was beginning to pull into the slow right-hand lane, and Philby caught a glimpse of two points of light in the out-side mirrow. It was too far to see if they belonged to the BMW. A series of diagonal yellow lines raced toward them as the fast lane began to narrow, and a sign loomed up showing two tapering vertical white bars with a red stroke across the middle: the end of the autoroute.

Philby knew this stretch of Switzerland fairly well, from studying Pol's Michelin map on their several gastronomic excursions into the surrounding French countryside. He remembered the double dotted red line that showed the proposed extension of the autoroute west to Martigny, then up to the Simplon Pass and into Italy.

He was thinking of the map that he'd seen on Demp-ster's lap. It could well mark the exact position of the road's progress. A row of luminous orange marker cones swept out of the half-light, directing them onto the main road around Montreux.

Peters reduced speed, to 140 kph. There was a slight bump as the Mercedes' front wheels struck the beacons, scattering three of them into the side of the road. In the same moment Peters switched the headlights on full, and Philby could see the surface ending about a hundred yards ahead at a row of red-and-white oil drums that blocked most of the road. Beyond stretched the broad white curve of the unfinished chalk road, with the edges straggling off into yellow clay.

Peters flicked the wheel and they missed the nearest oil drum with a swaying swoosh; then came a loud rumbling vibration and the speedometer needle dropped to nearly 120. This time, Philby twisted his head around and could see them, against the darkening sky, two bright points of light that swerved violently, then flared onto high beam, glowing off the ragged row of beacon cones.

The BMW righted itself, and its twin spotlights now came on, rippling down the edge of the last strip of surfaced road. It swerved again when it reached the oil drums, its distance steadily closing with the Mercedes.

Philby now realized what was going to happen, and in a confused moment wondered whether he should mention Dempster's map; but before he had time to speak, he was flung back against the stiffly sprung seat as the Mercedes surged forward, swaying slightly on the loose gritty surface.

They passed a column of mud-spattered yellow bulldozers and digging machines; then a huge dump truck swept into view, parked half across the road. Peters screeched around it, and the Mercedes began to slide into a slow dry skid. Peters' hands hardly moved, and just as slowly, he corrected the drive, almost without reducing speed.

The driver of the BMW seemed either less skillful or less lucky. Through the rear window of the Mercedes Philby could now see little but a white fog of chalk dust churned up under their wheels; but then he saw the lights of the smaller car slewing sideways until for a second it seemed to be held rigid, its headlights wobbling frantically across the edge of the clay bank. Then the long hard beam of a spotlight straightened again and settled back to follow the broken line of the verge.

The race went on for another seventy seconds. Ahead, the hills had turned black. The white chalk road snaked away under the two pairs of headlights, rounding a sharp bend as the Mercedes began to gain. Scattered lights glimmered high in the hills; several hundred feet below them, as the unfinished autoroute began to climb out along tall concrete stilts, they could see the blur of traffic on the distant main road running parallel to them along the lakeside. The white chalk kept coming on and on, thundering under the wheels and swinging into yet another bend around a dark shoulder of hill.

The wake of white dust was now so dense Philby could see nothing behind; and the next thing he knew, he was thrown forward against the painful pressure of his seat belt, then swung sideways against the corner of Peters' adjustable seat. One hand brushed Peters' shoulder, the other collided painfully with the door. He found himself half on his knees, the whole weight of his body suspended by the safety harness. There was a shriek and a howl of machinery that seemed to explode from under the floor of the car. He could smell burning rubber, and this time he was tossed to the other side, slamming his elbow against the window, and cutting his hand on the upper door handle; then his head bounced up against the padded roof and the floor came up to meet him as he flopped back again into his seat.

The whole incident had taken less than five seconds. During the last two, part of Philby's mind had registered the lights of the pursuing BMW. They had lit up the inside of the Mercedes with a distorting glare as the smaller car careered past them with a spray of flint and gravel that rattled off the Mercedes' windows, then vanished like a ghost car fleeing into the cloud of chalk dust.

Philby had time to see the cloud drift out into a pool of empty twilight, hang for a moment with the car's four beams of light waving wildly into the sky, then topple forward and plunge down into darkness.

Peters had cut the Mercedes' lights and engine; in the sudden hush, through the closed windows, came a faint clanking, crumpling sound. For two seconds there was silence again; then a dull boom, and ahead a white-orange glow swelled upward, outlining the column of naked concrete stanchions and the hard black line that marked the end of the autoroute.

Philby's door had jammed, and he had to slide out after Peters, his feet sinking into clay and his shoes scraping against lumps of rock. He saw that the Mercedes had spun around in its own length, leaving two scooped-out trenches of chalk blackened with scorched rubber, and had come to rest lying at a steep angle along the clay bank.

In the darkness the only light was the flickering glow from beyond the edge of the road. Behind were no lights, no sound. Peters and he walked together the thirty-odd yards to the brink. The road ended at a few rusted iron rods twisting out of a concrete shelf. Together they peered over. About three hundred feet below, the skeleton of a toy car was silhouetted in a ball of flame that was beginning to lick at the gorse up the sides of the ravine.

"Excellent work, Peters," Philby said dispassionately, and turned away; but Peters stood watching a moment longer.

Twenty minutes later, they joined the steep track up to

Pol's villa. Peters drove into the garage and let Philby go on ahead, up to the trellised patio, which was now lit by colored lanterns under the Moorish arches. Pol was still in his rocking chair, dressed now in a butterscotch silk suit and a heavy matching cravat. He was still drinking champagne, and rose with some difficulty to greet Philby. "You've hurt your hand, my friend? Nothing more serious, I hope."

"Nothing. The fish bit; we pulled in the line and fried him. There'll be a few red faces tomorrow in Whitehall —especially when it comes to explaining what two of their officers were doing driving down part of an unfinished motorway."

Pol was giggling as a thick swarthy man in a white tunic stepped forward and handed Philby a dark whisky. He drank it in the rocking chair next to Pol and gave him a full account of the chase. Pol scarcely interrupted, except to stifle his laughter. When Philby had finished, the Frenchman laid a fat pink claw on Philby's knee and cooed ecstatically: "So our little *séjour* in Switzerland was not in vain—eh, my friend? Now you should have little to worry you. And we can start making plans."

Next evening Pol gave a small buffet dinner. Apart from Peters, who stood immobile by the door, and Pol's four squat blue-chinned manservants—whom Philby had recognized from the hijacking of the Troika-Caravelle—there were fewer than a dozen guests. They ssemed prosperous and polite and inoffensive. Only one caught Philby's attention, a thin dark man in a cheap brown suit, with crooked cheeks and one white eye like a burned-out flashbulb. Philby recognized him at once as an Arab, probably of humble origins.

Pol himself paid almost no attention to the man, pre-
ferring to concentrate on the food: *terrine de campagne,*
salmon mousse, artichoke hearts, and strawberries and
cream served with Château d'Yquem. One thing about Pol
struck Philby as out of character: not once did he see the
Frenchman drinking. Nor did the small brown-suited Arab
drink.

Quick to suspicion, Philby was aware that the little
man scarcely looked like one of those fat-cat oil emissaries
from Saudi Arabia or from the Gulf States, where ab-
stinence is *de rigueur.* Only one other Arab country
enforced the same taboos, and that was Libya.

Philby had nothing to go on—not a grain of evidence
with which he could even broach the matter with Pol, let
alone interrogate him. The Frenchman's business affairs
were wide and eccentric, and some paltry dealings with an
oil-rich Socialist state across the Mediterranean would
hardly be out of order. Yet Philby—for better or worse—
was still very much Pol's creature, and throughout the
evening, the ugly thought kept crossing his mind that Pol,
in his role as the supreme *deus ex machina,* might already
be planning to link the immature fanaticism of Libya to
that of a certain African state.

Pol would do it for money, Philby thought. He would do
anything for money. But more dangerous still, he would do
it because he enjoyed doing it—for the devious pleasure
of the game. And it was because Philby understood these
emotions so well himself that in moments like these he
came close to fearing Pol.

# 1 2 3 4 5 6 7 8 9
# 10 11 12 13 14 (15) 16

*It was the smell that finally attracted more peo*-ple to the spot. The local militia arrived and found the body of a woman who had been in the water for about two weeks. What was left of her face was badly mutilated. The Criminal Police in Gagra were called in and the body was taken to the morgue at Police Headquarters.

The autopsy revealed that it was the body of a well-nourished woman of between thirty-five and forty-five, and that she had died not from drowning, but from a series of blows to her head and face. The only item of clothing left on her was a pair of partially decayed nylon tights, of Western make; and buried in one of the swollen, pulpy fingers was a gold wedding ring. The hallmark was again Western, and an expert later identified it as of British origin. The corpse's teeth also contained some expensive fillings that were not typical of Soviet dentistry.

The Gagra Criminal Police at once began re-examining the file on a missing British woman who had disappeared eighteen days before from the Grand Hotel in Gagra on the day that she had checked in. Her name was Mrs. Joyce Eileen Warburton, aged thirty-nine, and she had been employed for the last five months in the English-language section of Radio Moscow.

The head waiter at the hotel confirmed that she had dined in the restaurant with a man who had spoken English with her, but who had ordered in fluent Russian. She had left the hotel with him shortly before midnight, and none of the hotel staff had seen them return.

Since the case concerned a Westerner, the file was now passed to the KGB Bureau in Sochi, who immediately informed Moscow. Dzerzhinski Square had a considerable file on Mrs. Warburton. She had been cohabiting with an Englishman, Maddox, who had been killed by a hit-and-run truck the same evening that she had disappeared. The truck had still not been traced. Furthermore, Maddox had been in the employ of a certain Charles Pol, whom the Soviet authorities suspected of being involved in the hijacking of the Troika-Caravelle to Finland seventeen days before—the day after the woman had disappeared and Maddox had died. But what interested the Committee of State Security was the fact that Mrs. Warburton for some months had been the mistress of H. A. R. Philby, who had himself disappeared on the same day that she had.

The day after the body was found, a squad of senior KGB officers arrived in Gagra and began a vigorous inquiry. They were helped by several events which had seemed unimportant at the time, but which now became crucial. Two days after the woman had disappeared, a skiff had been found on the shore a few miles from the town. It was found to be a hired boat that had been reported missing from the beach below the Grand Hotel. Next day an oar had been washed up, and three days later a schoolboy from Gagra State Primary had been seen showing off the broken shard of a second oar, which he said he'd found on the beach. A week later, two dilapidated pieces of female undergarments had appeared on the "free" market in Gagra. They were of good material, though badly damaged by sea water, and both had labels printed in Roman characters which turned out to be the name of a well-known department store in London. The stall hawkers protested that they had also found the garments on the beach, and were only hoping to sell them for a few kopeks. The police confiscated them, and now brought them out for a careful examination. One, a brassière, was found to contain bloodstains which matched the blood group of the dead woman.

Next, the skiff and the two oars were traced and also examined, and further traces of blood were found, particularly on the broken oar, which had also retained in its splintered edges several strands of hair. Both blood and hair again matched those of the dead woman.

The Criminal Police decided that they had a *prima facie* case of murder; and the KGB did not contradict them. The discovery of the body, with its connections with Philby, Maddox, and Pol, prompted the State Security officers to order a high-level conference. All that remained now was to establish beyond doubt the identity of the decomposed body. The murder of an Englishwoman in the Soviet Union was not a matter that could be left to routine detection; and it was decided to make an official request, through the British Embassy in Moscow, for a trace to be made of Mrs. Warburton's dental history.

From her Social Security file in England, Scotland Yard tracked down a dentist in Exeter who had made a number of fillings in her teeth. Arrangements were made for him to be flown to Moscow, then down to Sochi, where the body was now being stored. He was a cheerful little man, who had been thoroughly enjoying his trip until he vomited twice during his examination of the body. But his files confirmed without doubt the identity of the late Mrs. Joyce Eileen Warburton.

The Soviet police had meanwhile been pursuing inquiries about the visitor who had dined with her the night she disappeared. Here they did not allow themselves to be deterred by the ubiquitous agents from Moscow. They were professional policemen, and except for treason, murder is the highest crime in the Soviet penal code. The fact that the murderer might also be a traitor did not concern them. He was a common criminal—the perpetrator of the brutal killing of a foreign woman on Soviet soil, and it was their duty to see that he was brought to justice.

They obtained three descriptions of the man: besides the head waiter at the hotel, there was the woman in the railway buffet who told them how a man had arrived in the small hours to catch the night express to Sochi. She remembered his exhausted state, which she'd taken for drunkenness; his scuffed shoes and slovenly appearance. Then there was an elderly Georgian who had had the bunk below him on the train, and who now volunteered a detailed description to the police, following an announcement in the local newspaper. The man had talked in his sleep, he said, in a foreign language. And when each of these witnesses was shown a photograph of Philby, they all identified him.

After a second conference in Dzerzhinski Square, it was decided to pass the case back to the Central Bureau of Criminal Police, who would pursue the matter through Interpol. The KGB decided to treat the incident as a lucky break; for although Philby's disappearance had not yet been made public by either side—no doubt for sound tactical reasons—the Committee knew that when the news finally leaked out, Moscow's embarrassment would be greatly offset by their being able to prove that Philby was not a master triple agent, but merely a squalid killer who had lured his mistress out in a stolen boat, battered her to death with an oar, and left her to the fishes.

The Criminal Police assembled the relevant documents and affidavits and presented them formally to the British Embassy, to be passed on to Interpol in Paris.

*Kim Philby entered Rhodesia as effortlessly as*
Horne had predicted. At Salisbury Airport he spent half
an hour with an exquisitely polite young Immigration
officer who, after granting him permission to stay three
months—renewable on demand—spent most of his time
detailing the pleasures and relaxations of Rhodesian life,
most of which struck Philby as being of a depressingly
outdoor nature.

The officer had seen at once that Philby was a gentleman.
He accordingly recommended to him the best hotels, clubs,
and spots for fishing and golf and sightseeing. Visitors
from Britain, he explained, were normally granted honor-
ary membership in even the most exclusive clubs, for an
Englishman who ventured into the "rebel" camp was
treated almost as a resistance hero—living proof that the
old links with Imperial loyalty still held.

After their interview, Philby took a taxi to Meikle's
Hotel in the city center and checked into a large old-
fashioned room, ate a wholesome English dinner by himself in the hotel restaurant, then drank himself to sleep
with the duty-free Scotch he had bought on the plane up
from Jo'burg.

He had arrived in the southern continent by a route of
his own choosing, despite the fact that Pol had provided
him with a first-class ticket on South African Airways
direct to Johannesburg. Philby had allowed Pol to see

him off at Geneva Airport; then at the last moment had canceled his reservation and transferred to a Swissair flight for Rome. There he had picked up a British Airways VC 10 on to Nairobi, where he had waited five hours for an Air France flight to Johannesburg.

Throughout the journey he had carefully avoided even the most casual conversation, while handsomely exploiting the free drinks served on the first-class decks and at the duty-free bars during stopovers. But never once did the old skills and instincts desert him, and by the time he was being checked, rumpled and rheumy-eyed, through South African Immigration at Jan Smuts Airport, where they seemed only interested to know if he was carrying a copy of *Playboy,* he was certain he was not being followed.

For over the past few months Philby had come to face an unpleasant truth. He did not trust Pol. He admired him, he was amused by him, he even liked him; yet behind that grotesque, giggling, clowning exterior, the Frenchman was one of the few people whom Kim Philby had found to be totally, unashamedly wicked.

In his long and varied career, Philby had worked for many odious masters. He had served them all faithfully, stealing, betraying, killing, while always fearful of being betrayed or killed himself. At the same time he had connived to save his own skin, and always enjoyed the spurious hope that someday he might be called to the aid of Mankind. So far he had survived, and now the part of Mankind that he had been chosen to help was the Black Man in White Africa. Help the old porter who had carried up his bags and bowed without a word as he accepted Philby's enormous tip. Help the half-naked children who romped in the dust around the shacks along the road from the airport; the placid workers he'd seen riding on their rusty bicycles from the tobacco fields, while the Europeans drank long drinks on long chairs in the setting sun and talked about adultery, bankruptcies, bridge, their children's schooling, and the price of liquor.

Philby had convinced himself that he'd come to Rhodesia to help change all that. He also knew that it would take time. London had made it clear they weren't going to rush him. But it wasn't London who worried him. It was Pol. Philby knew that without Pol, London could never have arranged his escape from Russia. But now, mortgaged to the Frenchman and his gang of mercenaries, Philby felt far less at ease than he had done under any of his former masters in Soviet Intelligence; for the Russians had always represented a professional, impersonal elite; while Pol was something else altogether. Pol was an amateur, a freebooter who hired out his services to the highest bidder. And Philby was uncomfortably aware that in his own case Pol had received a substantial payment from the funds of the British Secret Service—which meant the luckless British taxpayer.

The real problem was, just where did Pol's responsibility to London end? Pol was a man who liked to play the field; and from various incidents during their stay together in Switzerland, Philby was now convinced that the Frenchman was involved in dealings with certain Arabs. Arabs who had the same motives as London, only stronger? International Arab revolutionaries with limitless petro-dollars to finance whatever operation they had hired Pol to execute? And where did Philby fit in this new scheme of things? For Philby was still officially London's man, had been sent into Rhodesia as a low-profile, long-term agent. A sleeper. While Pol and his new paymasters —in Tripoli, or Algiers, or Bagdad—might have no use for sleepers. After all, the antiwhite struggle in southern Africa was very much a thing of the moment. Pol might easily decide that Philby, like the miserable Maddox before him, had become an embarrassment; and Philby had no illusions about how Pol would react.

Philby had always been careful not to inquire too closely into the Frenchman's immediate or long-range plans. Both discipline and experience had taught him never to question the tactics of a superior, though there were moments when he bitterly resented not being consulted. But what troubled him most was a detail that, during the dramatic, furtive planning with Pol in those last weeks in Moscow, he had foolishly, even wantonly, neglected. Before fleeing from Beirut, he had left implicit instructions that if he—Harold Adrian Russell Philby, only son of the great St. John Philby—should ever be arrested or meet with a violent death, his final testimony, lodged in a vault in Berne, should be offered to every newspaper in the Western hemisphere, together with the Director of Public Prosecutions in London. But H. A. R. Philby was no longer H. A. R. Philby. He was now an aging rake called Duncan Henry Saunders, and he had papers to prove it. Nor did he any longer have his old Soviet passport. Those lawyers in Berne knew of his redefection, of which he'd informed them on his first day after leaving Sweden; they were even aware of his new identity. But would this second affidavit invalidate the first? Those honest Swiss burghers had taken their instructions many years ago, and this sudden change of plan could so easily be a ruse, a forgery—by London, even Moscow. Both London and Moscow now hated him, and would smirk at the irony of his fate; and above all else, lawyers hated confusion.

The lawyers would ponder the situation, and probably

decide to adhere to their original brief. The death or disappearance of Duncan Henry Saunders would be of no interest to them. The second affidavit would be filed away and forgotten—like Philby himself.

But Kim Philby was no coward. On his first morning in Salisbury he decided on a course of "business as usual." He called first at the head office of the largest bank in Rhodesia, where he met with the same genial welcome that he'd received at the airport. As Horne had said, a true Britisher with a blocked sterling account was a man to be respected in this landlocked citadel of the Imperial dream. And Philby was dismayed to find how easily he was accepted as one of the dreamers. All chums together— the better class of White Man holding his own against the menacing hordes of disorder and darkness.

The manager was a large fleshy man with a powerful handshake and dissipated good looks beneath an overfresh tan. He invited Philby into his inner office and offered him South African gin and tonic. His name was Freddie Frobisher and he was president of a club called "The Abominable Snowmen," whose members were all expatri-ates with frozen assets in Rhodesia. On their second drink Kim Philby was invited to a party next evening.

"You'll find a lot of the old troopers there," said Fro-bisher. "And we've got a special consignment of Haig— brought over from Beira by a very fly chappie. Can't breathe his name, though—damned strict on security round here." Then, quite casually, he turned to the mat-ter of Philby's account. He called in a young clerk and told him to look up Saunders' file. "Seem to remember that we've been sitting on your lot for some time," he added. "Must be quite a bit of interest that's built up."

The file was brought with surprising speed. "Perishing

bore, this Sanctions business," Frobisher said, passing the folder to Philby. "But what I maintain is, there's a lot worse places to spend your money in than Rhodesia. A friend of mine reckons that the post-UDI crop of girls are about the best looking you'll find anywhere in the civilized world." He raised his glass. "Splash your money around and enjoy y'self while there's still time, that's my motto."

They parted finally, pumping hands and promising to meet next evening at the party, which was being given by a certain Randolph Grant—"known to everyone as 'Randy,'" Frobisher added. "Frightfully good mucker. He's run through four wives—all absolute stunners, except for the current one, and she's stinking rich. He now screws about everything that moves. He's also a great chum of P. K.—y'know, van der Byl, our illustrious Minister of Information and Immigration."

Philby left him with a sense of achievement: P. K. van der Byl was one of the Old Guard of hard-liners who'd been in the Smith government since UDI. But unlike most of his stiff-lipped colleagues, he had a sense of humor, and was known to be sometimes outrageously indiscreet. Philby decided there might be a useful opening there.

The next thing he did, after leaving the bank, was to buy himself a gun. He chose a .32 Beretta pistol, which he obtained simply on production of his passport. He had been a fair shot back in his SIS days in the war, and he planned to keep himself up to the mark with plenty of practice. Then, following a hearty lunch, he went to a leading real-estate agent and consulted a list of houses to rent. There seemed to be no shortage. He wanted something neither too central nor too secluded: a bachelor house where he would be allowed his privacy, yet not be too exposed to interlopers. The agent recommended an address on Cambridge Drive, in a quiet residential area seven minutes by car from the city center. It had a garden and swimming pool, and separate staff quarters for an African couple, who the agent assured him were thoroughly reliable. The rent seemed to Philby absurdly low.

The agent drove him out to the house and he found it to be exactly what he wanted. It was between two larger houses, which were both occupied; there was a high fence between the gardens, and the back of the house looked onto a long lawn that offered no obvious cover. The African couple were middle-aged, with a well-drilled servility that Philby found a relief, as well as mildly repulsive. In Moscow, private servants had been almost impossible to find, and equally difficult to keep.

The house was also fitted with the most modern locks, on windows as well as doors, and an alarm system connected to the nearby police station.

He drove back with the agent, signed the papers, paid a deposit and six months' rent with his virgin checkbook and walked out into the clear autumn sunshine with that familiar feeling that once again he was a stranger come home.

It was already dark when he arrived next evening in a hired Datsun at the address which Frobisher had given him, in the smart suburb of Highlands.

A pair of Africans in gold-braided tunics and red tarbouches stood inside the door and bowed him through, without even asking his name. The party was already well under way. A crowd of at least two hundred stretched from a large patio, with buffet table and barbecue, across the lawn to the swimming pool, which was garlanded with colored lights. Another African in braided tunic handed him a whisky and he began to move cautiously around the edge of the throng. Some of the men wore dinner jackets, but most were in either tropical suits or blazers and grey flannels. There were also many RAF mustaches, and from the snatches of conversation he heard, Philby concluded that most of them were as common as dirt. A cut above second-hand car dealers and scrap merchants, but only just. What he used to call the Saloon Bar Road Hog types —appearing now like aging ghosts from the England of the thirties.

The women, in unseemly contrast, were very up to date: a lot of long-legged girls in mini-skirts and kaftans, the older women in trouser suits or dresses that were too young for them, their complexions taut and leathery from too much sun and dieting.

Philby at last found Freddie Frobisher among a group by the swimming pool. The bank manager greeted him like an old friend, hailing him as "Our latest Abominable —Duncan Saunders—and he's loaded!" Frobisher's face was dark and moist, as he pulled Philby toward him and introduced him to their host.

Randolph Grant was an enormous man with rough handsome features, in a dinner jacket that could only have been cut by the best of London tailors. Philby sensed at once the raffish nonchalance of the well-bred bounder: now holding forth with the ease of a seasoned socialite. Grant turned from his audience, which included several very pretty girls, and looked at Philby.

"Another Abominable come in from the cold?" he roared; and biting into a cigar, he wrung Philby's hand. "What's your line? Copper? Tobacco?"

Suddenly Philby was stopped by his stammer. Despite Grant's boisterous exterior, his eyes were small and shrewd; he didn't look like a man who missed much. Philby covered his embarrassment with a gulp of whisky, then began answering the question just as Horne had instructed him. Grant asked a few questions, but they were mostly laconic, tossed at him as though to keep the conversation going. Philby replied to all of them with Horne's meticulous catechism; and Grant soon seemed to lose interest.

Philby's ordeal ended when a girl in a see-through blouse cried: "Tell Mr. Saunders how you came to Africa, Randy! About the boat trip when you were skint!"

"No jumbo jets in those days," said Grant, draining his glass. "I got a French tub out of Marseilles to Mombasa—steerage, with about four hundred stinking wogs with their prayer mats, all locked below decks like cattle. I was the only white man there. But on the second day the skipper took pity on me and gave me a third-class cabin, sharing with three Benedictine monks. When they weren't saying their breviaries or being seasick, we all played gin rummy, and because they were skint, like me, we played for Benedictine. They had a whole crate of the stuff, and they were damned bad players. I was soon drinking two bottles a day." He broke off, looking around him. "Where are those bloody munts? I need a refuel." A man at the back hurried off toward the patio.

Philby found himself next to a middle-aged man in a well-worn dinner jacket, standing with his feet apart, like a sailor on a heaving deck.

"First time you've met Randy, Mr. Saunders?" he asked, in a thick voice.

"That's right," said Philby. "I'm new here."

"He's a shit," the man said, and drank some whisky. "My name's Fielding, by the way. James Fielding. People call me Jimmy. I'm an Abominable, like you. Glad to meet you." He put out his free hand and lurched slightly.

He was about the same build as Philby, with the same lined face and scruffy grey hair, and his voice was slurred and cultured. Philby recognized an awful mirror image of himself, and felt an uneasy empathy with the man. Not only was there this physical similarity between them; there was also the astonishing coincidence that "Fielding" was the name Philby had chosen for his phony British passport, with which he'd boarded the Troika-Caravelle in Leningrad and reached the sanctuary of the West. There was another bond he shared with Fielding. They both disliked Randolph Grant. Philby had hated Grant on sight—hated him with those deep reflex instincts of the class struggle that had been instilled in him far back in the thirties, and that had marked his social conscience like a tattoo ever since. What had really appalled him about Grant was the way the man had been so ready—like everyone else in this country—to accept him as one of their own. Accept him into this fraternity of brash middle-brow bullies whom Philby had been fighting all his life. My God, he thought, I can't be as bad as that!

He and Fielding stayed by the pool drinking, while the party swayed and cavorted around the glow of the charcoal fire, like a ritual dance to the pious attendance of the African servants, who kept them freely supplied with the contraband whisky from Beira.

James Fielding was not a stimulating companion, and finally went to sleep in a long chair by the pool. Philby made his way over to the barbecue and had a few more drinks with Frobisher and his gang, while their host was absorbed with the attentions of a tall redhead—despite the presence of his latest wife, a formidable South African Jewess whose main attraction was said to be her share of a factory that had the concession for blankets to the Bantu townships.

Soon after midnight there were rumors that P. K. might show up; then came sniggers that he was "otherwise engaged." And about two o'clock everyone came to attention while the National Anthem was played on a gramophone. The older guests stood rigid, with heads high, but several of the younger ones chattered and giggled. Philby took his leave soon afterward. He was modestly satisfied with the evening. He had established himself without ostentation, had made a few contacts, and one friend.

He drove home carefully, watching out for the numerous police patrols, who were quick to catch drunken drivers; and before going to bed he made sure that all the doors and windows were secured, and the alarm system switched on.

Three days later, at 11:17 in the morning, a bomb exploded in Salisbury's largest supermarket in the city center. There were over two hundred people in the building at the time, most of them European women. Fourteen were killed instantly, five died in the hospital, and a total of fifty-eight were injured, of whom seven were permanently maimed.

The explosion took place near the entrance; the windows of the surrounding buildings were blown in, and a number of people were treated for cuts and shock, including a young woman who found a high-heeled shoe lying on the pavement with a foot inside it.

The bomb was believed to have been left in a canvas shoulder bag, and to have consisted of about thirty pounds of gelignite, detonated by a sophisticated time fuse. The police had cordoned off the area within minutes and questioned every shopper in the building, particularly the African and Colored staff. Nobody could remember anyone coming in with a canvas shoulder bag, and there had been no suspicious Africans lurking about just before the explosion. But one woman in the hospital was able to describe a short swarthy man, whom she'd taken to be an Italian or Greek immigrant, carrying two bags and making a number of random purchases, picking items off the shelves and tossing them into the bags as though he were on a shopping spree.

One of the African woman cashiers thought she remembered him, too, because he had paid with a Rhodesian twenty-dollar bill and seemed in a great hurry to get his change. She also thought he'd left only a few minutes before the explosion. It was the one lead the police had.

By noon the news had paralyzed the city with a dull rage. African terrorists were the obvious suspects, though the police were disturbed by the ease and efficiency with which the outrage had been carried out. The possibility of it having been the work of European terrorists was not yet being even rumored in the bars and drawing rooms of Salisbury. The nightmare of all whites in southern Africa—the appearance of a well-trained European terrorist movement—was still too awful to be openly entertained.

Kim Philby had no such doubts, however. He saw both the appalling reason and the virtue behind this latest of Pol's atrocities. For the moment Rhodesia seemed deceptively impregnable, enjoying the protection of her powerful neighbor to the south, and of the more doubtful Portuguese empire to the north and east. She remained a kind of nature reserve, where instead of wild life one saw the last of a tame but moribund species—the gin-and-tonic descendants of the Memsahibs, acting out the splendors of the British Raj in an affluent society that fed on Japanese cars and TV sets showing Portuguese programs; on German stoves and Italian fridges; Portuguese wine, South African beer, and Chinese clothes from Hong Kong. It was a becalmed society, a false society. In his heart every white Rhodesian knew that he was dreadfully vulnerable.

Their greatest danger was a simple but insidious one. Most of them were recent European immigrants who enjoyed a safe prosperity in a pleasant climate. But once that safety ceased, and the prosperity began to wane, many of them would cut their losses and run—forsake their outlying farms and comfortable town houses, and seek the gilt-edged security of South Africa. Rhodesia would quickly become an embattled enclave where a handful of poor whites struggled stoically against hordes of mutinous blacks—a miniature Congo, a second Algeria, another dismal monument to Colonialism, sliding into the same lethargic chaos as the rest of black Africa.

Kim Philby now saw his main objective as not so much to infiltrate Rhodesian society and unmask the prominent Sanction Busters, as to stake out strategic nerve centers for targets of terrorism: restaurants, bars, clubs, hotels, shops, banks, big commercial buildings; factories and industrial complexes; railway junctions and airports. The odd well-placed bomb, the random "necessary killing," would be enough to instill panic and despondency, and the rot would soon spread. Rhodesian morale would be sapped, and the bumptious Rhodesian Front would have to answer for the growing wave of terror. Mass emigrations would follow, and the white Rhodesian state would begin to crumble.

These were the dreams and aspirations that Philby enjoyed during his first few weeks in the country. He had little else to sustain him. No word came from Pol, though this did not worry him, since Pol had said he preferred to let Philby lie low and establish himself. Nor had London made contact. They usually ordered their regular local agents to make contact first—sometimes waiting months before identifying themselves. There were times when Philby wondered whether James Fielding was London's man, and was biding his time, as well as keeping a wary eye on him. There was nothing in the man's demeanor to arouse any direct suspicion—but from his own training Philby knew this was nothing to go by.

He continued to see Fielding several times a week, usually for their lunchtime drink at Meikle's. These were not joyous occasions, but they afforded Philby one advantage. He was still nudging his way into the upper crust of Salisbury society. It was a closed society, and discriminated strongly in favor of those it felt worthy of them, and to these it extended a voracious warmth and sympathy.

On this third week Philby felt able to give a small cocktail party of his own. He invited Freddie Frobisher and Randy Grant, their wives, and a number of hangers-on, as well as Fielding. Grant arrived late with a junior Minister—a small prune-faced man who'd been in the Royal Navy and got quietly drunk—while the rest of the party went with a swing. Philby had managed to get hold of some Scotch, through a contact of Frobisher's; and there was also French brandy and Havana cigars, acquired by a friend of Fielding's from Cape Town.

Philby was careful not to get too drunk himself: not that he feared giving himself away, only that he might transgress some subtle border line of behavior that would offend his guests. He followed Horne's advice: "You'll be expected to drink like a fish, but hold your drink like a man. They expect you to get *decently* drunk."

Apart from parties, his life was a quiet one. He even took to smoking a pipe—which he hadn't done since before the war—and went so far as to pay large sums for his favorite English tobacco. His most immediate problem was getting hold of the news. In Moscow no one had frowned at his habit of collecting his airmail edition of the *Times* each day; but here he had to be more careful. A few British papers were to be found, usually a couple of days late, at the big newsagents, and these were bought up as soon as they arrived; but most were subscribed to by known or suspected opponents of the régime. Philby got around this dilemma by ordering the *Daily Telegraph*, which was considered to be reasonably respectable, and had it openly delivered to him at the Abominables' Club, which occupied spacious premises opposite Meikle's. He told his fellow "Snowmen" that he couldn't do without the British sporting news—an explanation that was accepted without reservation.

Otherwise, he played a shrewd game of bridge, tolerable backgammon, and was even persuaded to try his hand, with less success, at golf. As far as he knew, his old reliable charm was still working and everyone he met liked him and asked to see more of him.

By the end of his first month in Rhodesia he had made probably more friends than at any time in his life, and was accepted as a true Rhodesian gentleman.

In his fifth week, he received a telegram at the *poste restante*, dispatched from Geneva the night before: SEE

YOU HOTEL POLANA LOURENÇO MARQUES FRIDAY 8 PM—
CHARLES. The message was in English.

Friday was two days ahead, which gave him time to
apply for his Portuguese visa to Mozambique; then he
booked a flight for Friday afternoon on Rhodesian Airways. He also telephoned the Polana Hotel, to be told
that a room had already been booked for him by a
Monsieur Cassis, who was also staying in the hotel on
Friday. Pol's effrontery rather shocked Philby, who had
been steeped in the lore of security all his adult life. Pol
was a conspicuous person in any community; and his face
had already been splashed across the world's press in
connection with the Troika-Caravelle incident. Yet he
now dared to expose himself on Philby's doorstep, when
a letter, or even an intermediary, would have surely done
the job as well. Unless, of course, Pol had some special
reason for coming so far.

Philby also realized that Pol's hold over him was as
firm as ever, and not for one moment did he seriously
entertain the idea of not going to the rendezvous; for he
knew that if he spurned Pol now, his continued existence
in Rhodesia would not only be rendered impotent—it
might be put in real danger.

He told no one of his visit to Mozambique—not even
Fielding, who in any case had left the day before on a
two-week visit to a remote but fashionable hotel called
Hillcrest, just north of Umtali, close to the Mozambique
border. Fielding had been particularly depressed lately;
he had been hitting the bottle hard, and friends had
urged that a stay in the mountains might do him good.

At 4:30 on Friday afternoon Philby stepped off the
Boeing 707—one of the régime's triumphs of Sanction

Busting—and walked through the sticky heat of Lourenço Marques' Vasco da Gama Airport. It had been raining and a yellow haze hung over the heaving, grey-green skin of the Indian Ocean. By the time he reached the terminal he was sweating. He was also struck by the number of black and brown faces mingling with the sun-tanned new arrivals; and realized, with a sense of shock, how subtly he had been infected by the semiapartheid of Rhodesia, where non-Europeans merely formed a neutral background, as impersonal as a bus queue glimpsed from the back of a comfortable car. He even found himself glancing suspiciously at the Portuguese Immigration officer—a sallow man with crisp black hair and distinctly simian features.

The twenty-minute taxi ride into the city took him along the coastal plain, burned brown by the long summer, past groups of handsome African girls in tribal costume offering themselves laughingly to the white visitors.

Philby had heard that Lourenço Marques had the reputation of being the Paris of the southern hemisphere; but his first impressions were of another ragged modern metropolis—shanty towns crumbling at the feet of highrise blocks, most of them unfinished, like steel skeletons straddling the few old Portuguese houses, whose stone frontages now looked forlorn and abandoned.

The European Continental myth persisted only along the wide muggy boulevards, with their pavement cafés and open restaurants which boast the famed L. M. lobster. Most of the cafés were crowded, often with soldiers in baggy green combat fatigues and soft-visored caps with canvas shields over the neck. Philby noted that well over half of them were African.

As they turned off the main Avenida, the taxi driver let out a yelp and pointed ahead. *"Vibora!"* he shouted with a wide grin. Philby looked ahead, and at first all he saw was the rear of a diesel-belching Army truck; then he noticed a silvery-grey coil spring from beneath the wheels and come rolling toward them. *"Serpente!"* the driver said, laughing.

Philby didn't ask what kind of snake it had been. Despite his love of animals he'd always had a peculiar horror of snakes. He hoped there were none at the Hotel Polana.

He was relieved to find that he had been given an air-conditioned room with sealed windows, overlooking the lawn and the ocean. He still had more than two hours before he was due to meet Pol. He gave the African porter five escudos and told him to bring him a large whisky sour. It arrived before he had time to undress and shower.

Later he wandered downstairs, into a lounge full of pink-faced men in shorts and long socks, drinking tea with their dowdy wives. The African waiters moved among them on slippered feet, while piped music played and a stock-exchange Telex chattered in a back room. The receptionist was pure Portuguese, with a soft in-gratiating manner, and Philby resisted the temptation to ask if M. Cassis had checked in yet, for he was still wary of being associated too openly with Pol.

As it was, at the precise moment that Philby was walking out of the hotel, Pol lay naked on the bed of his room—only two doors along from Philby's—talking on the telephone. He spoke in French, in slow, deliberate sentences, often repeating a phrase several times, or pausing to explain the meaning of some word. It was a conversation that would have meant little to anyone eavesdropping—even supposing the new Portuguese régime bothered to maintain their police surveillance. Nor was the number he had called of any significance; it belonged to an obscure international organization devoted to cultural welfare, and was situated in a black African capital to the north of Mozambique.

Pol was still talking when the taxi dropped Philby at a newsagent's on the Avenida de Liberdade, where he bought that day's South African English-language newspapers. He then chose one of the less crowded cafés and sat inside under a clanking fan, ordered a beer, lit his pipe, and began to read.

The papers were full of a fresh terrorist attack in Rhodesia, in which a carload of South African tourists, driving to the Rhodes Inyanga National Park on the Mozambique border, had been blown up by a land mine, killing all six passengers. Despite a massive security operation, no arrests had been made. It was the second outrage in three weeks that had yielded no result, and the Rhodesian authorities were clearly getting jumpy.

Philby chewed his pipe and tacitly acknowledged Pol's expertise. He could even imagine Peters—equipped with forged Rhodesian papers—volunteering as a reservist to help hunt down the killers.

At 6:30, as the street lamps came on, he strolled back down the Avenida and stopped for a drink at the Girasol —a circular penthouse restaurant-bar on the top of one of the city's tallest buildings. Its walls were of tinted glass and sloped out over the whole panorama of Lourenço Marques, past the domino patterns and necklaces of light, to the dark space of the ocean and the single red light marking the island of Inhaca.

It was the European cocktail hour and the place was crowded. Through the aquarium gloom Philby could just make out groups of smooth young men with lean, bronzed girls—mostly English South Africans over for the weekend, he decided—and nut-brown Portuguese with fat wives hung with jewelry, sipping Martinis and whispering money; and a few grey-flanneled Rhodesians swilling beer and talking sport. A sad-eyed African waiter in a white smoking jacket sat fingering the keys of a piano, tracing a blues melody. His was the only black face there.

A Portuguese waiter had stopped Philby, and was glancing around to find him an empty table, when Philby saw Pol. He was sitting with his back to the room, his head sunk into his great rounded shoulders, talking to a man who had his back to the window, almost looking at Philby.

It was eighteen years since Philby had last seen him, but he had changed little: thin, grey, self-effacing, in the sober three-piece uniform of the civil service. Roland Carter-Smythe, a permanent under-secretary at the Foreign Office, had called several times on Philby during his dog days in the mid-fifties, when they'd discussed his "pension" from the Service, following the Burgess-Maclean scandal.

The last time they'd met had been in a pub in Horseferry Road, just after the publication of the Government Paper that had formally cleared Philby of all allegations of his having been the "Third Man." Carter-Smythe had been very pleasant and discreet, but Philby had known that he didn't believe the official story. For Carter-Smythe was one of the hard-liners, and although Philby had never been able to prove it, he had been fairly certain that the man's FO title was a cover for Intelligence activities.

Philby reacted without hesitation. He apologized to the waiter, and unhurriedly walked out, along to the elevator and down to the street, where he asked the doorman to call him a taxi. His mind was clear, his nerves firm. Yet he was experiencing a sensation that he'd known once before in his life, back in Istanbul in 1944 when the Soviet agent Volkov had defected and Philby had come closer to being unmasked than at any time in his career—including Beirut in 1962, when he had at least anticipated a showdown and had been able to prepare his escape.

For like the Volkov incident, the sight of Carter-Smythe talking to Pol, in a far-off corner of the crumbling Portuguese Empire, caught him totally off guard. He felt exposed, helpless, even foolish. Yet as soon as he began to consider the matter more rationally, he realized that he should not have been entirely surprised: for the idea of Pol betraying him was certainly not new to him. This chance encounter in the Girasol only confirmed it. He'd always known that Roland Carter-Smythe had never been one of the pious mandarins who had agreed to the deal in Beirut; nor was he any diplomatic buccaneer who would lend his name to Pol's current activities in Rhodesia. Smith's régime might continue to be a nuisance to Whitehall; but the mere hint that the government was lending a hand to terrorism and murder in order to topple that régime would create a political scandal that would rival even the secret knowledge that Philby possessed.

Carter-Smythe could only be conferring with Pol for one reason. Kim Philby, alias Duncan Saunders, was to be written off.

By the time his taxi dropped him at the Polana, he had decided what to do. There remained forty minutes before his appointment with Pol. He ordered a stiff Scotch and sat down in the lounge to wait.

"Hit and run," Pol repeated in English, his lips dripping with melted butter. "Here, there—everywhere! In the important places—*les endroits de classe*—where the big people go, the rich, the snobs, the tourists. A bomb, *un attrape-nigaud*—how do you say it?"

"A booby trap," said Philby.

Pol nodded vigorously and his fat little hands ripped open a lobster claw, his fingers almost indistinguishable from the white meat and pink shell as he dipped it in the butter and scooped it into his mouth.

"You see the strategy?" he continued. "Hit, run, like the classic guerrillas, as the handbook says—to use the jungle like the fish use the water." He licked his fingers and reached for the napkin. "You, my dear Duncan"—he giggled—"you are like the barracuda. Or perhaps better, what you English call a Portuguese man-of-war?" And he relapsed into French: "Lying in the sea, your tendrils drawn in, waiting."

"Waiting for what?" said Philby. They were in a little restaurant by the port; from up the street came the baying of Afrikaners outside a strip-tease club that specialized in Zulu girls.

"I have planned a little operation for next week," Pol continued in French. "Something rather special that will upset your new compatriots. Something that will be quite a surprise!" He sat back and patted his belly. Philby waited, saying nothing.

"As I have emphasized," Pol went on, "security remains our top priority. For the moment the Rhodesian authorities are confused. They are not used to having the foxes escape from the poultry run. They know they are dealing with a well-organized unit, but they probably still suspect the Frelimo, or some other African outfit. Our great advantage is that they do not know who they are looking for. Once they do, they will change their tactics and our whole strategy will have to be revised. Therefore they must not find out. That is where you come in, Duncan." He paused to order another bottle of Mateus rosé.

"However, I think it better—for your sake—that for the moment you do not know too many of the details." He gave a grandiose shrug. "Just the remote possibility, you understand, that the plan fails and you are interrogated. Their methods of interrogation are very effective," he· added, "and far from scrupulous, particularly here in Mozambique." He sniggered over his wine, as though indecently relishing the idea.

"Come to the point," said Philby, in English.

"Yes. You have heard, I think, of the Hillcrest Hotel, between Umtali and Inyanga? A favorite tourist spot— very good for trout fishing, I understand."

"You intend to make it your next target?" said Philby quietly, still in English, while Pol continued in French.

"Not precisely. We intend to use it more as a rendezvous. You will meet us there—after you have satisfied us all that the terrain is secure."

"And how the hell do I do that? Cut the telephone wires?"

Pol looked at him gravely. "There is no necessity to use sarcasm, please. You will ascertain, for instance, that there are no police patrols around the hotel on Tuesday night—"

"Tuesday?" Philby repeated in French.

Pol nodded. "You will go to the hotel on Monday. If you have trouble getting a reservation, you must use what influence is necessary. It is vital that you be there."

"And how do I get in touch with you?"

"One of us will be in touch with you. By telephone, or possibly in person."

"But why can't you find out if there are any patrols yourself?"

"We could—but it would mean sparing an extra man. Our work is both dangerous and demanding. And besides, none of us are exactly English gentlemen. But you, Duncan—you have the perfect credentials to visit the Hillcrest Hotel. You will attract no unwelcome attention."

"Thank you," said Philby. "But you will have no objections if I take my own precautions? I am not known at the Hillcrest. I may decide to travel under an alias. In case, as you said, something goes wrong."

"An alias?" said Pol.

Philby smiled wearily. "I have a second passport, remember? Issued to me in Moscow by my kind protector at the British Embassy, Mr. Hann."

"But I understood that you surrendered that passport in Helsinki."

"That was the plan," said Philby. "But I never believe in doing anything in life without taking out proper insurance."

A sly smile crept over Pol's epicene features, then his whole body began to wobble with laughter. "Ah, you are a man of spirit and resource, my dear Duncan! And a man of caution, too. So, for the next week, you will cease to be Monsieur Saunders and become Monsieur Fielding again?"

Philby nodded and took a long drink of wine. A police siren wailed somewhere across the docks. A door banged up the street and there was yelling in Portuguese, followed by laughter. "It is, as I said, only a precaution," he added.

"And no one in Salisbury will know you have gone to the hotel?"

"No one. I don't have that many friends over there."

"Quite." Pol turned and snapped his fingers for the bill. "Monday night then, at the Hillcrest? And Tuesday we will contact you." He paid with a thousand-escudo note, leaving the waiter an extravagant tip, and asked for a taxi.

"I still don't understand why it was necessary," Philby said, "for us both to come all this way so that you could give me these instructions."

"Not necessary, perhaps," said Pol, "but advisable. I wanted to see you personally—see how Monsieur Duncan Saunders was comporting himself in his new role as expatriate." He put a finger to the side of his tiny nose and belched. "I prefer the personal touch, you understand? It is something that does not come with writing letters or talking on the telephone. I also like my instinct to guide me."

Philby did not inquire in what direction his instincts were guiding him this evening. When they reached the Polana, Pol was in high spirits and anxious that Philby should join him up in his room for a nightcap; but, on one of the rare occasions in his life, Philby declined. He preferred a quiet night, alone. He slept badly, however, and had one of his regular nightmares, waking with the sheet twisted around his body and soaking wet, despite the air conditioning.

When he finally rose and went down to breakfast, he found that Pol had already checked out. He had left no message.

Philby flew back into Salisbury that afternoon—a Saturday. The plane was full, and he had no reason to notice a small round-shouldered man in a rumpled grey suit who sat a few rows in front of him, holding a bulky briefcase. At the airport he had disappeared before Philby passed through Immigration.

His name was Paul Rebot; he was fifty-seven years

old, a law graduate and holder of the Croix de Guerre for his work in the Resistance, and for twenty-five years he had been a detective with the French Brigade Criminelle. During the last four of these he had been attached to the headquarters of Interpol in Paris.

His mission to Rhodesia was of a highly unorthodox nature, complicated by the fact that the Smith régime was not recognized by the 117 nations who subscribe to Interpol. Officially, Rhodesia remains subject to the writ of the British courts; and for the past month Rebot's superiors had been engaged in a series of intricate negotiations involving the British Embassies in both Paris and Moscow, secret conversations with members of the Soviet Diplomatic Service; and finally—the most delicate stage—contacts with the Rhodesian authorities. Here the first overtures had been made through an intermediary, an Anglo-Portuguese businessman resident in Beira, whose work took him frequently, and usually quite legally, to Salisbury.

While the chiefs of Interpol, who are mostly French, no doubt appreciate the diplomatic niceties of dealing with a blackballed régime, their work is not concerned with politics, but with crime. Political crimes, which include hijacking, as well as those loosely described as "having a political, military, religious, or racial character," are still outside their jurisdiction.

The case with which Rebot was now entrusted was on the border line. The crime was murder—the premeditated murder of a British woman in the Soviet Union. And murder is almost the only crime that is universally recognized as an extraditable offense. Even between countries that do not have a precise extradition treaty.

The complications had begun when the identity of the alleged murderer was given as a former Soviet subject, since stripped of this citizenship, to have it replaced by that of a bona fide British subject, born in Britain, and until lately resident there. The true identity of the man was not discussed, officially. All that concerned Interpol were the details of the crime, and the Soviet authorities had presented these in an impressive and convincing dossier. Interpol was satisfied, and so was London.

It was this dossier, together with a formal request for the extradition of the alleged murderer, that Rebot had brought with him to Salisbury, and which he now conveyed to a senior member of the Rhodesian Security Police, in a discreetly guarded house in the suburbs of the city.

The officer was called MacIntyre, a spare man with dry humorless features, deeply tanned and speckled with the benign cancer spots that come with long exposure to the sun. He had been a detective-sergeant with the Edinburgh Constabulary before emigrating to Rhodesia after the war, and still spoke with a Lowland burr which was deceptively reassuring. His manner with Rebot was studiously courteous. He knew most of the details already, but insisted that the Frenchman confirm the whole case from the beginning.

When it was over, MacIntyre grunted and rang for tea. "Highly irregular," he said at last. "Most highly irregular. We can surmise, I take it, who the man is? Even in this little backwater of the world, Inspector Rebot, we have our sources of information."

"London has not been entirely frank in this affair," said Rebot quietly; "but the motives of our British friends are not my concern."

MacIntyre nodded slowly. "Verry convenient for London, and, I might add, verry convenient indeed for the Rooshians." He put his big spotted hands on the pile of documents that lay in artistic confusion across the table, and nodded again. "There's just one wee matter that disturbs me, Inspector. As ye'll have heard, there have been several serious terrorist incidents in this country over recent weeks. It is not beyond the realm of possibility, do you not think, that this man may somehow be involved?"

Rebot sat with his hands on his knees, saying nothing; and suddenly MacIntyre gave him a bony grin. "If it's the man I think it is, I'll be gladly rid of him—don't you worry yourself about that. Some may call me and my kind rebels—but at least we're not traitors!" His grin hardened as he stretched out and detached one of the documents. "You will, of course, have realized that we have no extradition treaty with any country besides Portugal and the Republic of South Africa?"

Rebot replied, almost without moving his lips: "The Soviet Union has such a treaty with Zambia."

"Ah yes, Zambia." MacIntyre's hand slid back onto his hollow lap, still holding the document. "Yes, that might indeed be a most fortunate way of expediting matters." He looked down at the paper in his hand. "I assure you that on behalf of the Rhodesian government I undertake to comply with this order. However—with the greatest respect to you and your organization, Inspector—we would appreciate it if you would allow us a few more days before taking action. In the interests of our own security, as well as that of our Intelligence Service, it would be useful to observe the activities of this man a little more closely. He may have made contacts here in Rhodesia that would be of interest to us."

Rebot raised no objection. A room had been reserved for him at the Park Lane Hotel, and an unmarked police car drove him straight there from the meeting.

It was on Sunday morning, just before lunch, that Philby first realized that he was being followed. He was driving to Meikle's for his midday tipple when he noticed a blue Volkswagen about a hundred yards behind. It followed him to the corner of Cecil Square, and was waiting for him when he came out of the hotel half an hour later. There was only one man inside, reading a newspaper. Philby strolled across to the Abominables, collected his *Telegraph*, and had a drink with a few casual friends; then, not feeling hungry, he decided to drive out to Lions' Den and the Sinoia Cave, about fifty miles northwest of the city.

The Volkswagen followed him for the first fifteen miles. Then just outside Mbinga it disappeared. The driver had kept too far away for Philby to see him clearly, but he hadn't looked like any of Pol's men. A few miles farther on, he noticed a brown Renault driving at a steady distance behind him, although he kept his own speed down to less than 50 mph, allowing a number of cars to pass; then a few miles before Sinoia he pulled up at a gabled house with thatched roof and leaded windows, which advertised itself as "The Sundowners' Pub." He sat down at a table outside, and a moment later saw the Renault draw up, and a young couple get out and disappear into the pub.

He stayed long enough to drink a beer and let the couple inside make the necessary phone call. They did not follow him when he left; and five miles back down the road toward Salisbury he spotted the relief "tail"— this time a Land-Rover with two men inside. It stayed with him until he was two blocks from Cambridge Drive, then left him.

For the moment he was more puzzled than worried. The idea that Pol might be in cahoots with the Rhodesians seemed unlikely; a more plausible explanation was that London, or some section in London, had tipped off the Rhodesians; but for the time being—at least for the next twenty-four hours—he preferred the optimistic view that it was a routine screening that involved most newcomers to the country: that his open-handed welcome at the airport five weeks ago was now being balanced by a more thorough check by the Security service. What he absolutely refused to countenance was the possibility that by some slip of the tongue, or some flaw in Horne's briefing, he had himself aroused suspicion.

He stayed at home that night, cooked himself a curry, and drank himself to sleep. But in the small hours he woke from another nightmare—this time with Pol's naked body making love to the bloated corpse of a woman with no face. He got up and gave himself another drink; and in the silence of the house he began to view his situation in a less sanguine light. The police were shadowing him: there had been a leak somewhere—his passport, bank account, even a pro-Rhodesian agent in London. And for the first time since leaving Russia, he began to consider seriously cutting his losses and bolting.

He still had two lucrative and legal bank accounts outside Rhodesia. As for his identity, passports could be bought, forged, exchanged; he could vanish on the next plane down to Jo'burg, then perhaps go to the East, to South America, even to one of the Arab countries.

But by Monday morning, despite a painful hangover, his mood had become more aggressive. After all his varied fortunes, Kim Philby was not going to allow himself to be scared off by a few Rhodesian police thugs, or by a conniving Ananias in Whitehall, or even by the murderous Pol and his gang of mercenary butchers.

By lunchtime he had recovered enough to make a

boisterous entrance into the Abominables, where he ran into Freddie Frobisher and a crowd of his cronies. They had lunch together and Philby drank too much and had to be driven home. He was in no state to notice if any car was following them—though he had spotted one earlier, on his drive into town.

Then, in the late afternoon, when he'd slept it off, he discovered that his telephone was being tapped. He had put through a call to Fielding, and heard that brief silence, followed by the tiny familiar click as the dial tone started. Fielding had come on the line with forced cheerfulness.

"You'll be there later this evening?" Philby asked.

"Course, old man—where else? It's as dead as a morgue round here after dark. Don't think I can stick another week of it."

Philby had said he looked forward to seeing him again back at Meikle's and hung up; then instantly lifted his receiver and again heard the telltale click. He knew of subtler, less detectable ways of tapping a phone, but they were expensive, and he concluded that the Rhodesians were still unaware that they were dealing with an expert. To hell with them anyway, he thought. Only a few more hours to go.

He stayed in again that evening, and this time had the African cook prepare him a Spanish omelette; but he was not hungry, and did not even have the urge to drink. At ten o'clock he rang the Hillcrest again, but this time— after the listening-in click—there was no dial tone. He called the operator, and was told that there had been a fault on the line since seven that evening. Then, as he was leaving the phone, he felt a spasm of his old trouble —a sharp ache under the breastbone, which made him pause, panting for breath. It was several minutes before he could return to the bedroom and lie down; and he made a mental note to ask Freddie Frobisher to recommend him to a good doctor. It was nearly a year since his last checkup. He could not sleep; and by first light he had decided on a firm line of action. It was the kind of bold, outrageous gesture that his mad old father would have so well understood and appreciated. If London was willing to play games with Salisbury—and he had reluctantly come to the conclusion that somehow London must be involved—then he would start playing games with both London and Salisbury. His plan only needed the final confirmation.

He had just dozed off when he was awakened by the telephone. It was Freddie Frobisher. "Duncan? Heard the news? Bloody ghastly. Poor old Jimmy Fielding's dead—whole of the Hillcrest Hotel massacred last night! Fucking munts broke in and butchered the lot—women, several kids—two of them tots in their beds. Killed all the servants, too. Not a living person left. It's bloody war, I tell you."

Philby had some difficulty getting Frobisher off the line. Meanwhile, he had done his best to sound suitably shocked and horrified: although it was neither shock nor horror that he felt, but a mixture of relief and resolute anger.

He shaved and bathed, and twenty minutes later was outside Randolph Grant's house. He had driven fast and had seen no car following him. One of the African servants let him in, and kept him waiting several anxious minutes before showing him out to the patio, where Grant was sitting on a long chair, speaking urgently into a telephone, a cigar smoking away between his fingers. From somewhere in the house a radio was giving the latest news of the massacre at Hillcrest. No arrests had been made.

Grant waved him to a chair, grunted something into the phone, and hung up. "Hello," he said vaguely. "Heard the news, I suppose? Bloody business. Really bloody." He sucked at his cigar and frowned. "I'm afraid your chum Fielding was one of them. Sorry about that—he was a good mucker, I liked him." He breathed out smoke, and suddenly cried: "They'll damn well have to catch the bastards this time! My God, if they don't we'll have the lynch mobs out! People are angry, y'know. Doesn't take much to upset that stiff-upper-lip nonsense out here—not once those black monkeys get loose. My God, it doesn't!"

Philby said: "Randy, I've come to ask you a favor. Something vitally important to us all. I must talk to van der Byl."

"Christ, on a day like this? Not a chance. P. K.'ll be off his nut dealing with the reporters."

"I'm sorry, but it's absolutely essential that I talk to him. Immediately. What I have to tell him might—" he paused, controlling his stammer—"might have a bearing on what happened last night at Hillcrest."

Grant watched him screwing up his small eyes against the cigar smoke. "You choose your moments, don't you?" he said at last. "What sort of bearing?"

"I may know the identity of the men responsible for the attack. But I'm only prepared to give the information to van der Byl personally."

"You're not drunk, are you, Saunders?"

"I wish I were."

Grant nodded, stamped out his cigar, and lifted the telephone.

Barry Cayle was sitting under the oil lamp next to a pitcher of raw local wine, retyping the second chapter of his embryobook, *The Bored Man's Guide to Plain Cook-*

*ing,* when the old French laundrywoman came in with the telegram.

The dateline was London, and it had been sent that morning. URGENTEST AWAIT CALL 6:00 PM GODFREY. Cayle swore. It was now nearly nine in the evening.

He ran most of the way to the hotel, where he learned that there had been altogether eight calls for him, from both London and Paris. He again decided to defy standing orders, and booked his own call direct to the editor at the London office. He was still waiting for it when the ninth call came. It was the editor calling him. "Thank God! Where the hell have you been?" But before Cayle could answer, he went on, "You're going to have to move fast. Try to get to Paris tonight, or, at the latest, first thing in the morning. We've booked you on every available flight until tomorrow evening. After that you may be too late."

"Where to, for Chrissake?"

"Jo'burg. With a connecting flight to Salisbury, Rhodesia."

"Rhodesia! So I'm on a new assignment, am I?"

"You're on the same assignment, Barry. Only we can drop the hush-hush on the phones. The story's broken wide open. We got it early this morning. The Smith régime has announced it's holding a press conference—Thursday, 5:00 P.M., in Salisbury. And they're inviting just about every representative of the non-Communist press, radio and television networks."

"Sorry, Harry, I'm feeling dull. I'm just not with you. If it's a regular international press conference, you can get it off the wires. You don't need me."

"Yes, I do. You're the only one who has the whole background story—still exclusive."

"Background to what?" Cayle yelled.

"Simmer down," said the editor. "The point is we've had a strong report from two sources—and so far with no official denial—that the conference has something to do with your friend Kim."

"Holy snakes! What the hell's he doing down there?"

"That's what you're paid to find out. Now get moving. And if you miss that conference, I promise you I'll have you on 'Unmarried Mothers' for the next three weeks—part of a new series we're running on the social services. Ring me the moment you get to the airport. And good luck."

Cayle had to return to the farmhouse to fetch his passport, but did not bother to pack. He caught the last train to Paris with a couple of minutes to spare.

The door opened and the police sergeant sprang up with a scrape of his chair. Philby remained seated. Into the room stepped a very tall, lean man dressed in a black frock coat and stiff wing collar, his thick grey hair combed straight back from his forehead. His face was thin and hooked and very dark; and it was rumored by his enemies—of whom there were many—that the Minister of Information and Immigration had Indian blood.

He stood staring at Philby with his black vulpine eyes, while his long fingers caressed the silver top of a malacca cane. "Good evening, Mr. Philby." He gave a slight foppish bow, and sweeping back the tails of his coat slid into the chair vacated by the sergeant. "Enjoying your game?" he added, glancing at the checkerboard on the table between them.

Philby nodded sullenly. He was both repelled and fascinated by the man, who reminded him of a cross

( 295

between an old-fashioned head waiter and a stand-in for Count Dracula—although the effect was far from comic.

P. K. van der Byl turned to a stout red-faced man with a white mustache who had come in behind him and now stood beside the table, holding a grey plastic case. "This is Major Robson," he said, "one of our chief Security officers."

The red-faced man remained standing, glaring at Philby. There was a soft click as the sergeant closed the door and stood with his back to it.

"Now, Philby, I'm going to put you in the picture." The Minister leaned forward and placed his narrow elbows astride the checkerboard. "We have fully discussed your proposition, and in principle we agree."

"In principle?"

Van der Byl gave a very white smile. "I must beg your pardon, I was being pedantic—civil servants' language. It's one of the bad habits we pick up in government. Yes, we agree, Philby. We accept your conditions."

He went on smiling, as Philby said cautiously: "You've arranged full coverage? And I don't just mean your own press minions from here and South Africa. I mean the world press, even the ones that are *persona non grata*."

Van der Byl gave his little bow, which in no way dislodged his immaculate hair. "Of course. The British, Americans, French, Germans, Scandinavians, they will all be present. I only regret that your Russian friends will have to go by default. But then, no doubt they will take the word of one of their former colleagues?" His black eyes never moved from Philby's face.

"Now, the other half of the bargain. I have discussed the matter fully with the Cabinet, as well as our Security people. We've been doing some checking on the information you've already given us. So far it seems satisfactory.

We have been following some discreet inquiries through channels close to the French authorities. These confirm your description of the Frenchman Pol. Of course, here we will have to tread with some care. As you know, our relations with France, while officially still nonexistent, are by no means *cold*. It is essential, therefore, that we do nothing to upset them."

"What's happened to Pol?" said Philby.

Van der Byl leaned forward and began to fondle the silver top of his cane. "His little private army has been successfully *bagged*, as you would say. Thanks, in large part, to the information you have given us."

"And Pol?" Philby repeated.

Van der Byl tapped his cane gently on the linoleum floor. "I'm afraid that in the case of Pol himself we have had rather less luck. A warrant was issued yesterday morning to have him apprehended by the Portuguese. This was done as soon as he showed up at L.M.'s airport to take a flight to Nairobi. Unfortunately, the Security troops who accompanied him back into the city seem to have proved unreliable." He shrugged. "What can one expect, with this new crypto-Communist government in Lisbon? Anyway, the man Pol has disappeared. We were afraid at first that the troops had killed him. For we have since had reports that he was carrying on his person very large sums of money—mostly in Swiss francs and U.S. dollars. But Pol appears to have been too clever for them. The money he was carrying was in very high denominations, and we guess that he must have persuaded his guards that any simple Portuguese soldier trying to change such money would immediately attract attention." Van der Byl sat back and smiled.

"He's a smart fellow, this man Pol," he went on. "He got the guards to drive him to one of the biggest banks in L.M., where he made them wait outside in their truck, after giving them a solemn promise that he would return in a few minutes with the money safely converted into low denominations of escudos. After nearly an hour, the men outside began to get impatient. The senior officer finally ventured inside the bank. Of course, no sign of Pol.

"We've since learned that he spent twenty minutes with the president of the bank, who seems to be an old friend. The two of them then left by the private entrance at the back, and had an excellent lunch at the L.M. Yacht Club, during which Pol negotiated the hire of the hundred-foot cabin cruiser, the *Esperança*. He was last seen approaching Tanzanian territorial waters."

"How very frustrating for you," said Philby.

"Oh, but we still have you to make up for it! Now, for details. It is understood that you be our guest, as you requested, on a chartered plane to any destination you choose—within reason. South Africa, I would suggest, might be your most appropriate jumping-off point. Without prejudicing our friends down there, I can say with a fair certainty that you will not find too much difficulty in getting yourself fixed up with the necessary papers. As for money—well, I don't suppose you'll go short, will you?" He paused. "Have you any idea what you'll be doing? Afterward, I mean?"

Philby shook his head. "I never plan in public, Minister."

Van der Byl threw back his head and laughed—a loud, clear, oddly pleasing laugh. "Very good advice—I must remember it." Resting his cane on the floor, he rose with a smooth languid movement. "The press conference is planned for five o'clock tomorrow afternoon in Cecil Hall. I'm sorry about the delay, but we must give the press time to get here. At present, all we've announced is that a press conference is to be held on a matter of international importance, and that all existing restrictions on foreign newsmen will be temporarily suspended. In the meantime you will bear with us if we insist on you staying here. I'm sure it will be in your own interest."

He began to turn, with a swing of his cane, then paused and looked down at the checkerboard. "It seems you are beating Sergeant Pearce? So much easier than chess, of course. But then, I suppose you're also an excellent chess player? It's almost the national game in Russia, I'm told." He gave another bow, then nodded to the Sergeant by the door and walked out with long silent strides.

Sergeant Pearce closed the door again, and Major Robson sat down opposite Philby and, pushing the checkerboard aside, put the grey case on the table between them. It was a tape recorder, which he now began to adjust, punching buttons and testing the volume, before placing the hand microphone in front of Philby. "Right," he said, in a gruff English voice, "let's get started. I'll let you talk at your own pace, and give me everything you know about this man, Pol, and his organization. As a trained Intelligence officer yourself, I don't think I have to emphasize that even the most trivial details can often prove to be important." He pushed the recording button, sat back, and pulled out an old briar pipe. As he did so, Philby took out his tobacco pouch.

"Allow me, Major—genuine Three Nuns."

The man's face became even redder. "Oh, thank you. Thank you very much. Haven't tried Three Nuns in donkey's years. Most grateful to you, Philby."

Cecil Hall was ringed with police Land-Rovers and a double line of armed policemen—two white to every one black. By 4:30 the international press corps, heavily armed with cameras, sound booms, and batteries of lights, began to form an undisciplined queue up the steps, waiting to have their credentials checked. Near the front was the big, bent-nosed figure of Barry Cayle, in bush shirt and canvas trousers.

Inside, it was hot and airless under the glare of arc lamps. The three hundred seats were ringed by white police, both uniformed and plain-clothes. The stage was bare except for a table and three chairs, behind a row of microphones. Two plain-clothes men, their walkie-talkies jabbering inside their jackets, stood in the wings just out of sight of the auditorium; and behind them, in the corridors and adjoining offices, were groups of civil servants, government officials, diplomats. In one of these rooms sat Inspector Rebot and Chief Superintendent MacIntyre, flanked by a couple of plain-clothes men.

By 4:56 the press had been finally herded into their seats, with the television crews in the front; and at exactly two minutes to five the Minister of Information and Immigration strode onto the stage wearing a faultless dark suit and formal tie, followed by the small dour figure of Lardner-Bourke, Minister of Justice and Home Affairs. Kim Philby came last. He was greeted by a slow rustling murmur that swelled back across the hall, accompanied by the dazzle of flash bulbs, a few ironic claps and cheers, and a single solemn boo that was quickly silenced by one of the policemen around the wall.

P. K. van der Byl opened the proceedings, his long body stooping slightly forward, his forefinger resting on the table top. "Ladies and gentlemen. This, I venture to suggest, will perhaps prove to be the most unusual conference that any of you have had the pleasure of attending." He paused to move his head slowly sideways so that the cameras caught every angle of his saturnine profile. There was silence, except for the soft whirr of the cameras.

"My guest, ladies and gentlemen, needs no formal introduction. But for the record, and on behalf of Mr. Lardner-Bourke here and the rest of my colleagues in the Rhodesian Front, let me emphasize that our invitation to him in no way reflects the political or moral attitude of our government toward his career. However—" and he paused again, theatrically, bending farther forward— "what he now has to tell us may well reflect on the integrity of the permanent public servants of a certain nation, which since our independence in 1965 has seen it as its high moral duty to pass judgment on our own small independent country. When you have heard what our guest has to say, you may wonder whether these righteous gentlemen have the moral right to pass judgment on *anyone!*

"Ladies, gentlemen, I give you Mr. Harold Philby."

As the applause and catcalls died down in the auditorium, Inspector Rebot and Chief Superintendent Mac-Intyre were joined outside by a grey-haired man who whispered something to MacIntyre, then turned to Rebot and said, "I'm Colonel Dexter—Immigration. I'm very pleased you could come, Inspector." They shook hands. "The car's ready outside," he added; "and we have a special escort laid on to the airport. But all depends on absolute secrecy. Lusaka has confirmed landing clearance, on the condition that no word of the arrest reaches the press. So things here will have to be handled with the utmost discretion."

"You can count on that, Colonel," said MacIntyre, and

looked at his watch. "We're estimating that with questions he could go on for half an hour. The Minister will then wind up."

Dexter nodded. "Fine. I'll wait outside. I'd rather like to hear what he has to say."

"Plenty of time to read about it in the papers," Mac-Intyre said.

Philby had been talking for just over ten minutes, without a trace of stammer, his soft voice amplified across the hall, where the only movement was the scribble of shorthand and the occasional swing of a sound boom.

He looked tired and rather small under the lights. He spoke without notes, gazing out across the rows of faces, and sweating slightly.

"Now I come to what I believe is a matter of some historical importance. As I have already said, my motives in appearing before you remain my own concern. I know that many will criticize me, many will condemn me. But I wish to go on record as stating that in what I did, I was not alone. I was never alone. While I was working for the interests of the Soviet Union, there were others in my job—others far more important, far more powerful than I ever was—who were working with me in the same interests, for the same cause. Some of them are still working for that cause." He paused and closed his eyes against the lights; then, with what looked to some of the audience like a wince of pain, he reached inside his jacket. He stood for several seconds very still, then opened his eyes and slowly drew out a crumpled sheet of paper.

"Gentlemen—" he steadied himself against the table. "Ladies and gentlemen," he began again, "I am now going to read you the names of five men. They all hold high positions in Britain today, and three of them are still Her Majesty's principal civil servants—who are, and have been, to my certain knowledge, for more than thirty years—in the employment of the Soviet State Security Organization." He jerked his head down to the paper in his hand, dropped to his knees, and rolled over on the floor.

In the ensuing uproar, van der Byl called for calm. The two plain-clothes men in the wings were already leaning over Philby. He was breathing in quick gasps. The first journalist to reach him from the floor was Barry Cayle. Philby showed no sign of recognizing him. His eyes had become shiny slits and his face was like wax. One hand was still locked around the sheet of paper; the other fluttered beside him, then lay still.

"Someone get a bloody doctor, for Chrissake!" Cayle yelled. He was down on his knees, trying to prise the paper out of Philby's fingers. Then he saw Philby looking at him. There were bubbles of spit on his bloodless lips. His fingers released the crumpled piece of paper. Cayle opened it, then looked at Philby.

Above the noise, Philby started to speak. Cayle had to lean close to hear. "You d-don't think I'd be fool enough to put it in writing, d-do you?"

A beefy plain-clothes man pulled Cayle to his feet and shoved him back toward the edge of the stage. He was met by a crowd of journalists on the floor of the hall. "What's happened?" they cried.

"Heart attack, looks like. And what a time to choose!" He opened the piece of paper in his hand. It was blank. "He conned us all again. The bastard."